GREAT EVENTS
IN THE LIFE OF
KIT CARSON

lps Frémont win California
for the United States, 1846

6 Goes to Washington for Frémont
and sees President Polk, 1846

made Colonel of 1st New
Mexican Volunteers, 1861

7 Is appointed a United States
Indian Agent, 1854

D1207618

THE STORY OF
Kit Carson

Kit kicked his mule into a gallop

THE STORY OF
Kit Carson

By EDMUND COLLIER

Illustrated by NICHOLAS EGGENHOFER

ENID LAMONTE MEADOWCROFT
Supervising Editor

PUBLISHERS Grosset & Dunlap NEW YORK

To
KIT COLLIER
May your stick float true!

Contents

[v]

Illustrations

ILLUSTRATIONS

THE STORY OF
Kit Carson

"Well, children," he said, "here's your Christmas present."

CHAPTER ONE

Kentucky Christmas

THIS was a very important Christmas Eve. For once the Carson children were quiet and busy. There was an air of waiting around the log cabin on Tate's Creek.

It was more than the hush that comes before a fall of snow. It was more than the hope of coming presents. It was more than dreams of tomorrow's feast.

The children were waiting for a baby.

Their mother, Rebecca Carson, had said, "I only hope it won't come till after Christmas. There's so much to do!"

Pa Carson had patted her shoulder and laughed.

"Now, Becky, what's there to do the young 'uns and I can't handle?"

[3]

"Yes, Ma," ten-year-old Elizabeth said. "You always act like we're still children."

Her mother smiled. "I know you're growing up fast," she said, "but—"

"Buts butter no bread," her husband had said. "What better Christmas present than a baby? Rest easy, Mother. We'll do the work."

Now the tall father paced the floor of the log house. It was getting dark. He threw an armful of fat hickory bark onto the smoldering fire. Flames blazed up and lighted the room. They licked the big iron kettle that hung in the fireplace. The cornmeal mush cooking in it began to bubble. It sent out a hunger-making smell.

Father Carson looked up at the empty pegs over the door where his long rifle belonged. Will and Andy, his oldest boys, had gone hunting, because their mother wanted some fresh meat for Christmas.

"Don't worry, Ma. We'll get you a-plenty," Will had told her.

He and Andy had started out gaily yesterday morning. They'd been gone all night; and now a second night was starting. It was time they came back.

[*4*]

Pa glanced at the other children. Nancy was putting wooden bowls on the split-log table. Elizabeth was getting pewter spoons from the homemade corner cupboard. Young Robert and Hamilton were sitting solemnly on their peg-legged stools, chewing frost-sweetened raw turnips.

Footsteps sounded outside. The door opened. Moses stepped in with a pail full of steaming warm milk.

"It's snowing," he said. "When do we eat? I'm hungry enough to chew rocks."

Nancy came over and took the milk pail. "Supper's ready," she told her brother. "We've just been waiting for you to bring the milk. It took you long enough!"

"The old cow felt the snow coming and hid out in the canebrake," Moses said. "I had a time getting her in."

"No sign of Will and Andy?" their father asked anxiously.

"Nary sight nor sound," Moses replied.

"I hope they haven't run into Shawnees," Pa Carson said.

"Now, Pa," Moses scoffed. "Stop worrying. There's been no Injuns around for years."

[5]

"You never can tell when a band might sneak back," Pa said.

"Come on, boys, sit up," Nancy told her brothers. She swung the big black kettle on its crane out over the hearth. Then she began to ladle the golden hot mush into the wooden bowls.

Their father stepped outside. The snow was beginning to come down hard. Already a white sheet had covered Moses' tracks from the barn.

In front of the cabin, Tate's Creek flowed by under a skim of ice. Pa Carson strained his ears to hear above its rattle. An owl hooted off in the woods.

Then all was still again except for the rat-

tling creek and the soft swish of the falling snow. The worried father couldn't see ten feet into the white wall.

"If the lads get caught in this," he thought, "they'll never get home for Christmas."

The owl hooted again, nearer.

Another answered in a different tone. Pa cocked his head and listened. It couldn't be Indians. Moses was right. There hadn't been a raid for years.

The hoots came again, this time closer.

Suddenly Pa's face broke into a wide smile.

"The rascals," he said, and gave an answering hoot.

Then came the muffled pounding of hoofs on snow. Dark shapes loomed before him. Two mounted men with a loaded pack horse pulled to a stop.

"Well, I'm glad to see you," Pa said. "You just about made it."

"Just about, Pa," Will agreed.

"I see you got meat."

There was pride in the father's voice as his two hunter sons swung down and stood in front of him. They were as tall as himself. The Carsons were all big men.

[*8*]

"Yes, we got meat finally," Will said. "Deer and turkey. Had to go a fur piece for it. Chased a b'ar, but didn't catch him."

"Well, hang up your meat and come in," Pa told him. "Supper's waiting."

[9]

Will and Andy led the horses through the snow curtain to the barn. Then their father went back into the house. He stamped the snow off on the hearth.

When the boys came in, the younger children had finished their mush and milk. Sarah, the oldest girl, was filling more bowls. Pa Carson went over to the table and sat down with his older sons.

After supper they took their corncob pipes, and sat in front of the fire.

"I swear," Will said, "game's getting scarce. We had to go plumb to White's Lick, and we had to hunt for it even there."

"Is that a fact?" Pa asked. "I can remember when that place was thick with buffalo."

"Not a one left now," Andy said. "They tell me no one's seen a buffalo in Kentucky this year."

"Beaver's getting scarce, too. Selling beaver fur has been our best way of earning money. Next year we'll have a hard time to trap enough beaver to pay for the work," Will said.

"The oldtimers are heading west 'most every day," Pa went on. "Dave Kincaid took off just last week."

"It's ten years since Daniel Boone left here and went to Missouri," Will added. "But they say beaver's still plenty there. Let's move there too, Pa."

"Maybe, some day," Pa Carson said slowly.

The frontiersman and his three sturdy sons stared thoughtfully into the fire. Their eyes were gleaming with dreams of new lands.

After a while Pa got up to see how his wife was. The three older boys went off to their beds in the loft. The younger children had long since gone to sleep.

Christmas morning broke bright and clear. There were four inches of snow on the ground. The trees and bushes were woolly with it. From the creek came a muffled sound, like an old man snoring under a white blanket.

Excitement was in the air. The boys came down quietly from the loft.

There was the cow to be milked. Wood to be brought in. Deer to be skinned and butchered. Turkey to be plucked and cleaned.

Moses got his milk pail and tiptoed out. Andy followed him. Will laid oily hickory kindlings on the fire. He rubbed some cedar

[*11*]

bark into a fluff. Then he took flint and steel. He struck off a spark into the fluff. He blew on it till it burst into flame, and tucked it under the kindling.

In no time a blaze was roaring up the chimney. The girls crawled out of bed into the warming room.

An hour later the young Carsons were sitting at their Christmas morning feast. Fresh deer liver. Home-cured bacon. Golden corn bread. Pumpkin molasses. Milk in wooden cups called noggins.

The door to their parents' bedroom opened. Their six-foot father stooped through with a bundle in his arms.

"Well, children," he shouted, his face all smiles. "Here's your Christmas present—Christopher Carson."

All talking at once, they crowded around him. Will was the last to look. He peered at the tiny, towheaded, bandy-legged mite in his father's arms.

"He's kind of runty to go by such a long name as Christopher, ain't he, Pa?"

"Right," said Moses. "He might get his feet tangled in that long name and trip."

Pa Carson laughed. "We don't want him falling on his nose," he said. "We'll call him Kit."

Just then, the baby began to cry.

From the bedroom came their mother's voice.

"He may be little, but just listen to him yell!" she called. "When he grows up he's going to outdo the whole pack of you. You'll see."

And Rebecca Carson was right. Kit Carson was always small. But what he lacked in size he more than made up in grit. And when he raised his voice—which was seldom—people always took notice.

CHAPTER TWO

The Next Frontier

MAKE her sing, boy! Make her sing!"

"Her" was the Carsons' brand-new two-man saw.

The speaker was Pa Carson. The boy was Kit. It was September, 1818, and he was nine years old. They'd left Kentucky when Kit was about a year old. Now they were cutting down trees to clear a new field on their Missouri homestead.

Kit's father stood up and mopped his forehead. He smiled down at the boy. Kit was still towheaded, bandy-legged, and short for his age. But his shoulders were beginning to broaden and his chest to fill out. The tough life of the frontier had made him strong as a hickory sapling.

"Don't ride the saw, son," his father said. "Let her roll. Loosen up and take it easy. Then she'll sing. And when she sings, you'll know she's cutting wood."

They stooped to their work again. Kit did as he'd been told. The saw began to sing. Thick

shavings poured from the cut. The two-foot wide buckeye tree began to sway.

Pa shouted, "Watch out!"

They pulled the saw out of the cut and stepped back. With a great *whoosh* the tree toppled over. It hit the ground with a crackling of branches, and lay still.

Pa hung the saw in the fork of a little blue beech tree. Their lunch basket was hanging in the same tree. Kit looked longingly toward it. This was hungry work. The boy's stomach was hollow as an old log.

His gray-headed father looked up at the sun.

"Reckon it's time to eat?" he asked.

"Long past, if my stomach's a sign," Kit said.

Pa took down the lunch basket and passed it to Kit. He picked up his long Kentucky rifle that was leaning against a big sugar tree. Kit could tell that rifle anywhere. Its stock had been broken by an Indian bullet, and Pa had mended it.

He and his father walked over to the edge of the clearing where they could feel the breeze blowing up from the river. They sat down on a log and began to eat.

[*16*]

There were thick slices of ham, tangy from home curing over hickory smoke. There were big slabs of johnny cake. There was milk in a great gourd to keep it cool. There was plenty of everything, and Kit found it very easy to take.

The smell of ripe wild grapes hung heavily in the hot noon haze. Down toward the river a Negro boy Pa had hired to cut and burn brush was singing at his work. The smoke from his fire drifted toward them. It added its bit to the other smells of early fall.

Over on another part of the farm some of Kit's brothers were getting in corn and pumpkins.

There were fourteen healthy, husky children in the family by this time. Sarah was married. The older boys often went farther west hunting, trading, or trapping. Then the rest were pressed to keep up with the work.

Kit washed down his last slab of johnny cake with a swallow of milk. He slid off the log, stretched out, and half closed his eyes against the sun. It was a sleepy sort of day. The smoke from the river was getting thicker.

Kit limbered his muscles. They were pleasantly lame from sawing. He could feel them getting stronger. It looked as if he was going to be the littlest one in the middle of a family of big men. But he figured to work right along with any of them. Yes, and do better than they did at some things.

He looked up at his father, who was stoking his corncob pipe. Two fingers were missing from Pa's left hand. They had been shot off in an Indian fight. Kit wondered how Pa had trained himself to work so well without them.

Kit kicked with his heels at the fat, black bottomland. His father tamped down the tobacco with a firm thumb. He set it afire with flint and steel.

Pa turned his back to the river, and reached out for a handful of the black loam. He rubbed it between his fingers and let it dribble to the ground.

"It's nice, boy, isn't it?" he said.

"Sure is," Kit answered.

"It's rich as can be," Pa went on. "Wait till we get this piece plowed up. She'll grow more corn to the acre than any land we've turned yet."

"Is Mose coming home to plow?" Kit asked.

[*18*]

"I hope so. But even Mose has got that far-gone look in his eyes these days. Can't stay put —those lads. All they can think about is trapping in the Stonies."

The Stonies! Kit's eyes shone at the words. In his mind he could see the Stony Mountains with their high peaks sparkling in the sunshine against a bright blue sky—or at night glowing softly under a mountain moon.

White men mostly called them the Stonies, or the Rockies. But the Indians were poets. They called them the Shining Mountains.

Kit had never seen them. But he'd heard of them from his older brothers. Some day he'd go and see them for himself.

Kit's thoughts came back to the farm on the Missouri River. His father was still talking.

"Beyond this river there's nothing for you —unless you want to live like an Indian and trap furs."

Kit thought, "That's just what I want to do! Pa ought to know."

His father went on.

"Education. That's the thing. There's a great chance for a man with some book learning in America today."

[19]

Kit was half listening. Part of his mind was still in the Stony Mountains. The wind from the river was freshening. The brush-fire smoke was thicker. It made Kit's eyes smart, and he shut them.

His father's voice was louder.

"Kit, you're a smart lad," he said. "You ought to make use of your brains. The other boys are all bigger and stronger. Let them do the rough work. I want you to be a lawyer. I want one educated man in the family. I—"

At a sharp crackle behind him, Pa Carson broke off and turned.

Kit opened his eyes. A clump of dry brush had burst into flame. Fire was spreading from it and sweeping toward them. Kit jumped up.

The Negro boy shouted a warning. He rounded the spreading flame and came running toward the Carsons like a scared rabbit.

Kit felt a twinge of fear. "What'll we do, Pa?"

Pa was on his feet, sizing up the danger. "Got to build a fireline. Quick! Run to the cabin. Hook up the mules and bring back everyone—boy or girl—big enough to handle a tool. Get all the axes and shovels and hoes you can lay hands on."

CHAPTER THREE

Fire!

THE fire was spreading fast. There was a strong breeze behind it, and it made its own wind as it went. The faster the red fire traveled the stronger became the wind.

The Negro boy came up panting just as Kit turned to run for help. Kit could feel the heat on his back as he zigzagged through the woods.

Kit had good lungs. But by the time the cabin came in sight he was gasping for breath.

The land around the cabin had been cleared of big trees and brush, so Indians couldn't sneak in. But there was plenty of dry grass.

As Kit dashed up he managed to get out one cry of "Fire!" The boys in the cornfield beyond the cabin heard it. They came running.

He blurted out his story. In a jiffy they had the team harnessed. The girls came tearing out of the cabin. The biggest ones grabbed the rear of the wagon and were yanked aboard as the mules made off at a gallop. Kit clung to the sides of the bouncing wagon and tried to get back his breath.

As they got into the woods they had to slow down. Smoke seeped through the trees. It dried out their noses and made their eyes smart. Soon they could see the long red line of advancing fire.

The homestead lay in a protecting curve of the Missouri River. Two snaky creeks ran past the cabin and down to the river. At one point they bent toward each other. Here they were less than two hundred yards apart.

This was the best place for the fireline. The only place.

As the wagon came near, Kit could see the backs of his father and the boy bobbing up and down. They were working hard to clear away brush and small trees to make a line wide enough to stop the fire.

Pa's tall form rose up as the wagon came clattering toward him. The husky young Carsons piled out with their tools in their hands.

Pa wiped his smoke-blackened face. He gave orders. The youngsters spread out. Some with axes attacked brush and small trees. They threw branches back behind the line. Others with shovels and hoes dug fiercely at the duff —the layer of rotting leaves on the forest floor. They hacked at roots till their shoulders ached.

As Kit worked, the smoke got thicker and

thicker. Luckily they had thought to bring a bucket. One of the girls got water from the creek. They wet their handkerchiefs and tied them over their noses. That helped keep smoke out of their lungs.

The fire got closer and hotter.

"Ouch!"

That was Kit. A spark had fallen on his back and burnt a hole right through his shirt to his skin.

He glanced at his father, brothers, and sisters. All were working hard and fast. Their sweat dried in the fierce heat. The fireline was growing. One end of the fire lapped up to it and stopped.

At another spot, a bush close to the line exploded into flame with a frightening roar. The wind carried a shower of sparks across the line. Some went out in the air. Some hit the ground and slowly lost their glow.

Three or four sparks stayed lit. They burned little round holes into the dry duff. The holes widened. The wind fanned the glowing duff into flames.

Pa was hacking at a vine-covered dead buckeye that straddled the fireline.

"Watch those spot fires!" he yelled.

Kit jumped back of the line. He started hoeing around one of the spot fires. Hamilton, next oldest to Kit, came up and pounded it out with a shovel.

They put out all the spot fires before they got out of control. When the children turned back to the fireline it was almost finished.

But the vine-covered buckeye had caught. The soft dry wood was a tower of fire. Sparks were showering from it.

Pa was still hacking away at it. The tree had to come down or it would start spot fires all over the place.

Kit kept glancing at his father. Pa's face was grim. Kit thought he must be half roasted. The axe slashed in and out of the blaze.

Kit yelled, "I'll get the saw, Pa. We'll make better time."

His father called back, "You keep away from this tree! Get your fireline done."

And just then a big branch broke from high up on the flaming trunk of the buckeye. It hit Pa Carson hard on the head.

He swayed, toppled over, and lay still. Tight-lipped, Kit ran to him. Hamilton was

[26]

right behind. They dragged their father away from the heat of the fire.

The fireline was finished. The others gathered around Pa, silent, frightened. Their fa-

ther was pale, his eyes staring. "Bring the water," said Kit.

Elizabeth brought the pail of water. Kit began wiping the soot from his father's face. The children watched. They forgot all about the buckeye that their father had chopped almost in two.

The flaming tree stood swaying in the wind. Suddenly it broke off with a loud crack. It crashed to earth across the fireline. Flame licked out from it on three sides. A shower of sparks started more spot fires.

The children looked from their father to the new fire, not knowing what to do next. Kit decided quickly.

"Get that fire out!" he yelled. "I'll look out for Pa."

The others jumped to work. They dug and chopped hard and fast. Soon they had the new fire cut off.

They came back panting and sweating to where their father lay, and stared down at the tall, smoke-grimed figure on the ground.

Kit stopped bathing the still, pale face. He looked up at his brothers and sisters. He choked back his tears and told them.

"Pa's dead."

CHAPTER FOUR

Kit Runs Away

THE afternoon sun streamed through the big window of David Workman's saddle shop. Kit moved, so that the sun would not shine in his eyes. He pressed his foot down on the pedal of the saddler's vise. The jaws closed. They held tight the two sides of the stirrup strap he was sewing together.

Kit took pride in doing a good job. He was becoming a skilled leather worker. But he didn't like sitting still all day. And he didn't like the man who owned the saddle shop.

"I reckon Workman don't set out to be mean, but he sure does nag," Kit thought, as he poked a strong needle through a hole in the leather. "Wish I could get my gun and go hunting. I'll bet the water in the river ain't too cold to go swimming, either."

He sighed and looked across his high work-
bench through the big window. Before him
was the lively frontier town of Franklin. A
group of mountain men stood talking in the

square. Kit stopped his work to watch them. They were men who had been trapping in the Rocky Mountains, and they'd come to Franklin to get supplies.

Franklin was farther west than any large town in the states but St. Louis. Between it and the Rockies lay wild, unsettled Indian country. Far to the southwest was land that belonged to Mexico. A trail eight hundred miles long ran from Franklin all the way to the Mexican town of Santa Fe.

Pack trains and wagon trains went back and forth along that trail, day after day. Even now Kit saw a string of white-topped, boatlike wagons wheel past the window of the saddler's shop, headed west.

At the head of the train was a stocky man on a fine black horse. He wore a wide, flat black hat, and a suit of clean new buckskin.

Kit knew he was Charles Bent. Bent and his brothers were big-time traders with the Mexicans in Santa Fe.

"Santa Fe!" Kit said, half-aloud. "I sure got a hankering to see that place." He longed to go off with that wagon train.

His fingers grew still as thoughts filled his mind. It was eight years since his father had died. So far Kit had done nothing about getting an education—about learning to become a lawyer. Sometimes he felt guilty about this.

[32]

He would like to do what his father had wanted him to do.

But books meant nothing to Kit. Often, the saddler, David Workman, brought a newspaper called the *Missouri Intelligencer* into the shop. Sometimes Kit would look at the big letters in the headlines, and try to puzzle them out. But he never tried very hard. He was more interested in hunting and fishing than in book-learning.

Suddenly his thoughts were interrupted as the bell above the door tinkled. He heard someone come into the shop.

"Daydreaming again, eh?" came a whining voice.

Kit turned. It was bad enough to have Workman catch him idling. But it was worse to be caught by the man in fringed buckskins who was with him. For this man was Tom Fitzpatrick, who owned the saddle Kit was supposed to be mending. Tall, strong, black-bearded, ruddy-cheeked Fitz was a real mountain man.

"Mr. Fitzpatrick wants his saddle this afternoon," Kit's master whined on.

"He'll have it," Kit answered sharply.

[*33*]

Kit was a very quiet boy. He was seldom rude. But he wouldn't crawl to anyone.

Workman was angry.

"None of your lip, Kit," he scolded. "You're bound to me for three years. If I catch you loafing again, I'll take a strap—"

Kit jumped from his stool and faced Workman. For months he'd stood for the man's nagging. Now a strange fire was sweeping through him.

"You'll what?" he said. His voice was quiet but deep.

"You heard me," whined Workman, his face flushing. "Get back on that stool—"

Kit's eyes flashed. He was too angry to know what he was doing. Springing at Workman, he grabbed him around the throat. In an instant the man was on his knees with his eyes bulging and his tongue hanging out.

Tom Fitzpatrick gripped Kit's wrists and pulled them away from the saddler's neck.

Kit stood up, trembling.

"Take it easy, boy," Fitzpatrick said calmly. "You almost killed the man."

Kit gulped. "I know it," he said, wondering what had come over him.

[*34*]

Workman stood up and leaned against the
bench, panting. He glowered at Kit.

"We'll see about this," he gasped. "I'll have
the law on you."

Suddenly the rabbitlike man darted out of the door. Kit and Tom Fitzpatrick watched him scurry down the street toward the jail.

Fitz chuckled. "Now you've gone and done it, lad," he said. "What's a fighting man like you doing at a saddler's bench, anyway?"

Kit grew calmer as he looked up into the steady eyes of the mountain man. Kit knew about him. Fitzpatrick was one of the best trappers in the West.

"I've got to learn to earn money somehow," Kit answered.

"A lad like you could make more money in the mountains in three months than you'll make here in the next five years," Fitzpatrick said.

"But I'm bound out to Workman. Ma signed the papers," Kit explained.

Fitz snorted. "Bound, is it?" he said sternly. Then his voice softened.

"Listen, lad," he added in a kindly tone. "You're a free-born American. No one can make a slave of you—but yourself."

Kit's eyes began to shine.

"If only—" he began with slowly growing excitement.

[36]

Fitz put a hand on the boy's shoulder, and looked deep in his eyes.

"Would you like to go west?" he asked.

"All my life I've wanted to," Kit told him. "My older brothers are trappers. They've been as far as Santa Fe. But Ma never would let me go with them. She says I'm too young."

"The life of a mountain man is hard, you know," Fitz warned.

"It can't be worse than sitting still all day sewing saddles," Kit objected.

"All right," Fitz went on. "That was Charlie Bent's wagon train that just went through town. He's heading southwest with stuff to trade to Indians, and to the Mexicans in Santa Fe. He's aiming to camp awhile a few miles beyond the Missouri River. If you don't wait too long, you might catch him before he starts off again."

Fitz stopped speaking as the doorlatch behind them clicked. He and Kit turned toward the sound.

The door opened. Workman and the town marshal, Zeke Hall, walked in under the tinkling bell. Kit stood stiffly against the bench as the pair came up.

[37]

Tom Fitzpatrick stepped clear. Out of the corner of his eye, Kit could see the heavy Green River knife hanging in its scabbard at Fitz' belt.

Hall stood solidly in front of Kit. Workman hovered behind.

"What's this I hear, Kit? What's this nonsense about trying to choke your master?" the marshal asked sternly.

"I guess—I guess I lost my temper," Kit admitted. He stood up straight and faced the marshal squarely.

Hall eyed Kit sadly for a minute. Then he said in his heavy voice, "Mr. Workman has taken out a warrant for you, Kit. I've got to arrest you. I've no choice."

Kit said nothing. Hall took a pair of handcuffs out of his pocket and stepped closer.

"Hold out your hands," he ordered.

Tom Fitzpatrick's voice cracked like a whip. "Don't do that!"

Hall turned, startled. His hand began to creep toward the gun at his hip.

Fitzpatrick said nothing. He made no move. Kit watched him, his eyes wide. Workman began to shake.

[*38*]

Kit glanced again at the broad-backed Green River knife in the trapper's belt. He thought the tall man could be quick with it.

Fitz' eyes as he glared at Marshal Hall were as sharp as the blade of the knife.

Hall swallowed twice. His hand stopped creeping toward his gun. He took out his handkerchief and wiped his forehead. Then he turned and walked toward the door. The saddler padded after him.

[39]

Tom Fitzpatrick turned to the boy. His eyes crinkled in a friendly smile.

"Here. Give me that strap you were working on," he said.

Kit handed him the stirrup strap from the bench.

Fitz put the strap in the vise. He began to sew like a trained saddler. Kit watched him with growing admiration.

The trapper gave him a sharp glance.

"Are you going to stay here till someone wraps a jail around you?" he asked.

Kit got the point. He took off his apron and hung it on its hook.

He opened the back door. As he stepped out he paused for a last glance at the mountain man.

Fitz looked up.

"If you catch up with Charlie Bent's wagon train," Fitz said, "tell him I sent you. You'll never find a better man to take you to the Rockies."

CHAPTER FIVE

The Wagon Train

IT WAS a dark moonless night. An old brown mule splashed out of the Missouri River and stumbled up the western bank. Kit stumbled along beside him, clinging to his mane with one hand, and struggling to hang onto his father's big rifle with the other.

He was shaking with cold. His teeth were chattering. He was hungry and lonesome.

They stopped on the bank while old Brown caught his breath. The boy looked back across the river. Behind Franklin the eastern sky was growing gray. Lights from the lamps of early risers were showing in the windows of the town.

"We better get moving, old mule," Kit said, "before someone sees us."

He shouldered the long rifle and turned away from the river. Then, walking to keep warm, he led the mule west over the prairie.

Fitz had said the wagon train was a few miles beyond the river. Kit wondered how many he meant by "a few."

Soon the rising sun began to warm Kit's back. But it did nothing for his hunger. As the sun rose higher and higher, he grew hungrier

and hungrier. He climbed on the mule, who moved more and more slowly.

Kit was beginning to fear the wagon train had left. But just before noon he rode to the top of a swell in the prairie and saw white-hooded wagons in the distance.

Then Kit began to worry. He was a sorry sight. His blue jeans were covered with mud. Half the buttons were off his hickory shirt. His sandy hair was a tangled mess.

He was riding bareback with only a frayed rope for a bridle. The stiff-kneed old mule was plastered with mud.

Kit felt a sudden sinking in his stomach. "Bent'll never hire us," he thought. "Everybody'll just laugh."

The mule had no qualms. As soon as he saw the wagons he stretched out his neck in a fast walk.

Kit started to pull him in. Then he changed his mind.

"If you're not scared, old mule," he said, "I guess I hadn't ought to be."

He dug his homemade moccasins into old Brown's ribs. The mule lumbered to his fastest gait, a sort of rocking-chair lope.

As he came nearer the wagons Kit saw that they were drawn up in a hollow square. One corner was left open so the stock could be driven in and out.

Inside the wagon square everyone was busy. New mules were being broken in. Wagoners were mending harness. Cooks were feeding fires under black kettles of sowbelly and beans.

But as the bedraggled boy and rattle-boned mule rode in, they all looked up from their work. Some began to laugh and hoot.

"You should've buried that mule outside," a rugged teamster shouted.

Kit set his jaw and looked straight ahead. He saw Captain Bent sitting on a wooden box near the middle of the square. Bent's fringed buckskins were almost pure white. They were bright with colored beads and dyed porcupine quills.

"Some difference between his clothes and mine," thought Kit.

But he rode straight for the captain and stopped.

Charles Bent looked up with round black eyes at the serious-faced boy. Those bright eyes twinkled as Bent took off his wide-brimmed

[45]

He rode straight for the captain and stopped

beaver hat and scratched his shock of thick black hair.

"What can I do for you, boy?" he asked.

"I'm looking for work, sir," Kit said. "I'd like to go west with your outfit."

Standing beside Bent was an old, old man. His tanned face was lean and lined. His hair was gray and thin. His buckskin shirt and leggings were grease-blackened. Half the fringes were gone.

But the long rifle on which he leaned was clean and shiny. And his blue eyes were sharp as an eagle's.

"What do you think, Dave?" Bent asked the old trapper. "Shall we give him a job?"

"It kind of looks like the mule's too old and the boy's too young," drawled David Kincaid.

Just then a young rider dashed into the square and pulled his horse to a rearing stop.

Kit knew him. He was a Franklin boy who earned money by carrying mail and messages between town and the wagon trains. He gave Kit a quick glance. Then he turned to Bent.

"Can I see you alone?" he asked.

"Why not?" Bent answered.

The messenger dismounted. Leading his

[47]

horse, he followed Bent behind one of the wagons.

Kit slid off the old mule and stood leaning weakly against the beast's side.

He feared the messenger would tell on him, and Bent would feel bound to send him back to Franklin. So far he'd been held up by excitement. Now he felt very, very tired.

Kincaid had been eyeing the gun that the boy still clutched by the barrel.

"Where'd you pick up that rifle?" the old man asked.

"It was my father's," Kit told him.

"How'd the butt get busted?"

"Got hit by a bullet in an Injun fight," Kit replied.

"Tate's Crick in Kentucky, warn't it?" asked the man.

"Yes, sir," Kit said. "Before I was born. How did you know?"

"I was there, son," Kincaid replied. "You must be a Carson."

"I am. Lindsay Carson was my father."

"He was a good man," Kincaid said slowly. "I reckon if he was still alive you wouldn't be in this fix."

[48]

Charles Bent and the messenger came around the wagon. They were heading straight toward Kit. Bent had a newspaper in his hand.

Kit pressed back against the mule, his heart beating fast. But he sighed with relief when the messenger got on his horse and rode off.

Bent came over and sat down on the wooden box again. He laid the newspaper open on his knees. Kit saw it was a copy of the *Missouri Intelligencer* that was published in Franklin.

Bent's eye scanned an item in the paper. He took a red sandstone pipe from an embroidered leather pipe glove that hung around his neck. Thoughtfully he tamped home a bowlful of tobacco.

Then the captain peered closely at Kit from under his heavy black eyebrows. He tapped the item in the paper with the stem of the pipe. "Listen," he said, and began to read.

"NOTICE: To whom it may concern: That Christopher Carson, a boy about sixteen years old, small of his age, but thickset, light hair, ran away from the subscriber, living in Franklin, Howard County, Mo., to whom he had been bound to learn the saddler's trade, on or about the first day of September last. He is supposed to have made his way toward the upper part of the state. All persons are notified not to harbor, support, or subsist said boy under penalty of the law. One cent reward will be given to any person who will bring back said boy.

(signed) DAVID WORKMAN

Franklin, Oct. 6, 1826"

Bent laid down the paper. He puffed at his pipe and looked at Kit for a moment more.

"Could this be you, by any chance?" he asked.

"Yes, sir."

"Your master don't value you very high— one cent."

Kit said nothing.

"Are your parents living?" Bent went on.

"My mother is. Pa died eight years ago."

Old Kincaid interrupted the questioning.

"The boy's all right. His pa was Lindsay Carson—a true man if ever one lived."

"All right, Dave. But this fellow's a runaway. I've got to know the whole story."

He turned to Kit again.

"Does your mother know you've run away from Workman?" he asked.

"Yes, sir. I went right home. She gave me Pa's gun and the old mule—"

[50]

"Where you been since then?"

"Hiding out," Kit replied. "They had the bloodhounds after me."

"Hm," said Bent slowly. "You must've done something besides just skip out."

"Well . . . I did, sir," Kit agreed unhappily. "The saddler kept nagging me till I finally went for him. Tom Fitzpatrick said—"

"Tom Fitzpatrick? What's he got to do with it?"

"Well, sir, he held off the marshal from jailing me. And he told me to find your wagon train and tell you—"

"If Tom Fitzpatrick sent you here, there's no need to say more," Bent said. "Anything Fitz says shines with me. You can come along with us and help herd the extra mules and horses."

"Thanks. Thanks a heap," Kit gulped. "I wouldn't want to get you in trouble, though. If the boy that brought you the newspaper reports to the marshal that—"

"Don't worry," Captain Bent broke in. "Franklin law doesn't reach this far. If that marshal tries to push it any farther, we'll give him some gun-talk."

The captain turned to old Kincaid.

"Fix the lad up with a couple of Mackinaw blankets, Dave, and whatever else he needs."

Kincaid put a gnarled hand on the boy's shoulder. "Come along, Kit," he said. "The

blankets can wait. First we eat. You're as thin as an old cow at the wrong end of a hard winter."

Kit filled himself to bursting with hot beans, bacon, and coffee. He was so tired he almost fell asleep with his tin cup halfway to his mouth.

Kincaid gave him a pair of red and black Mackinaw blankets. He laid down a buffalo robe under one of the wagons. Kit flopped on the soft brown hair, and pulled his new blankets over him. He stretched and yawned comfortably.

Tired as he was, he was happy. Soon the wagon train would be rolling toward the West. The big adventure was about to begin.

In his mind, Kit saw the high peaks of the Rockies shining before his eyes as he fell asleep.

CHAPTER SIX

The Santa Fe Trail

T URN out!"

The cry of the wagon master rang through the cold October dawn. Kit opened his eyes.

"Yup, yup, yup, yup yaow!"

The yells of the night herders sounded out on the prairie. Then the sudden drumming of galloping hoofs. Horses, mules, and oxen came pounding toward the wagon corral and poured through the entrance.

Kit pulled on his moccasins and jumped to his feet. Ropes whished. Chains jingled. Dust filled the air as teamsters caught their mules and hitched up.

Out of the dust came Kincaid leading a snappy black mule.

[*54*]

"Roll up your bedding and throw it in the wagon," the old trapper told Kit.

As Kit obeyed, Kincaid said, "We turned your old mule loose. He'll follow along. Think you can ride this one?"

Kit said nothing. He took the reins from Kincaid and swung into the saddle. The black mule turned his head and looked at the boy. He nipped at the stirrup. Kit poked him in the nose with the toe of his moccasin. Then he kicked him in the ribs with his heels.

The black mule almost jumped out from under him. He twisted in the air like a snake. Kit rode it out. In a minute he circled the animal back to the old man. Kincaid had a broad grin on his face as Kit rode up to him.

"That mule goes by the name of Satan," he said, "but I guess you're his match."

"He's a good strong mule. I like him," Kit said.

"For the job you're going to have he'll need to be strong."

"What job is that?"

"Herding cavvy."

"Cavvy?"

"Yeah. All the extra mules, horses, and

oxen. You'll have to help drive 'em along behind the wagons. And you'll have to take your
turn herding the cavvy at night."

By this time the teams were all hitched and
ready to go.

"Stretch out!" yelled the wagon master.

Whips cracked. One wagon moved out. Another pulled alongside. The rest fell in line.
Kit rode Satan back to help herd cavvy. The
eight-hundred mile journey to Santa Fe had
begun. It would take nearly two months.

Slowly the long train of white-topped wagons moved toward the southwest. Day after day the men traveled over the grassy prairies, and camped when they came to water.

One night they were sitting by the campfire when Kincaid said to Kit, "Have you ever seen any buffalo, boy?"

"I never have," Kit answered.

"It won't be long now," Kincaid told him. "Then you'll have to learn to shoot your own meat."

"I'm willing," Kit said, his eyes sparkling at the idea of a buffalo hunt.

"Don't let me catch you bringing in any tough old bull," Kincaid warned him. "Fat cow's what we want. And there's only one way to down 'em. Ride up on the right side. When she moves her front leg forward, you'll see a bare place. Shoot down and into that spot. Get the lungs. They'll run off with a hole in their heart—sometimes."

Kit listened carefully as the old trapper went on to explain all the tricks of buffalo hunting. Two days later they came to a stream early and made camp. Kit took the old rifle and rode out to see if he could find some meat.

He crossed the stream and rode westward. He pushed Satan up a high, grassy rise. At the top he pulled in the mule. Wonder filled his eyes at what he saw. For miles the plain was black with buffalo!

The great shaggy beasts were grazing toward the south. The huge heads on their massive shoulders hugged the ground as they busily cropped the rich grass. Tall, white buffalo wolves followed the herd and snapped at the stragglers.

Kit's heart beat fast. Did he dare go down there alone and try his luck?

"Reckon I'll have a try at it," Kit thought. He dug his heels into Satan's sides and forced him down the slope.

An old bull on the outskirts of the herd raised his head and snorted. Beyond the bull Kit saw a fat cow. Other buffalo looked up. They started to move off.

Forgetting fear in his excitement, Kit kicked his mule into a gallop. The buffalo near him began to run. Kit came alongside the cow. He pointed his gun at the right spot and fired.

At the bang the whole herd was off like a

rocket. Kit tried to reload and keep up with the cow. She began to bleed at the nostrils. In a moment she stumbled and fell down dead. The herd swept by.

Kit got off his mule. He tied Satan to the dead buffalo's horn. Then he cut out the tongue and hump ribs. He wrapped them in a piece of the buffalo hide, cut a slit in it, and hung the bundle on his saddlehorn.

The sun was getting low as Kit mounted and headed toward camp. Behind a hillock he heard a faint bellowing and some wolflike snarls that made shivers run up and down his spine. Riding round the hill, he saw a very old bull which had not been able to keep up with the herd. A pack of buffalo wolves were snarling and snapping at the poor animal.

The old bull kept turning his head to ward off one attack after another. But the wolves were too quick for him. He was bleeding from many wounds and gasping for breath. Kit felt sorry for him.

A huge wolf closed in for the kill. Kit brought his rifle to his shoulder and fired. He caught the wolf in mid-leap. It twisted in the air and fell writhing to the ground.

[59]

The other wolves ran off. But the blood smell of the old buffalo was strong. They stopped on the nearest ridge and looked back. When Kit made no move to shoot them, the great white beasts sat down on their haunches with their tongues hanging out and waited for him to go away.

But Kit had decided to get himself a wolf-skin. Leading Satan close to the dead wolf, he tied him to a greasewood bush. The old bull was still standing near by, panting heavily, too tired to move on.

The sun set as Kit leaned over and began to skin the dead wolf. As he worked, the other wolves came slinking down from the ridge. Kit didn't see them till one leaped at the old bull. Then he reached for his gun.

From a kneeling position he aimed and pulled trigger. No sound! He'd forgotten to reload. A huge white form rose in front of him. He raised the rifle to ward it off. But the wolf bowled him over. The pack was on him snarling.

And then—a rifle cracked. Like dry leaves in a gust of wind, the wolves scattered and ran away. But they left another of their pack dead.

As Kit sat up, he heard the clatter of hoofs, and then Kincaid was looking down at him sternly.

"How was it your gun didn't go off?" he asked.

Kit looked him in the eye. He blushed. But he wouldn't lie.

"I forgot to load it," he said sheepishly.

"Never do that again," the old man said earnestly. "If you're that careless, you'll not last a week in the mountains. Lucky thing I come looking for you. Next time, let me know when you leave camp."

Kit saw his friend was more frightened than angry. He was glad he'd told Kincaid the truth.

They skinned the two wolves and rode back to camp. Kincaid never told anyone about Kit's carelessness. He just gave the boy credit for bringing in the buffalo meat and the wolf-skin.

Kit was grateful. He remembered the lesson even after he was grown up. It helped him become one of the most careful men in the mountains. Other men made him their leader because they knew he would not carelessly lead them into danger. And because of his honesty he became one of the few men trusted by both white men and Indians.

CHAPTER SEVEN

Payday

WEST went the wagons. Wheels clunked. Whips popped. Guns barked as riders out front cleared the trail of rattlesnakes. Coyotes sang on the ridgetops. Herds of buffalo opened up to let the wagon train through.

The land had been rising all the way from the Missouri River. When it began to rise more sharply, Kit began to look for the mountains. Kincaid said he could see them a hundred miles away.

At last, one day, they had stopped for a long nooning. Kit sat on a wagon tongue, chewing a juicy hump rib of buffalo. As he strained his eyes into the west, the dust from the halted caravan slowly settled. Suddenly Kit's eyes widened. A faint far line was taking shape.

Kit jumped to his feet. He blinked and

looked again. No mistake. There were the Rockies! Kit could see them clearly now. Their great blue masses were piled one behind the other high into the sky.

"Dave, look!" Kit shouted. "The mountains!"

Old Kincaid came over and stood beside him. "You've got sharp eyes, lad. You're the first to spot them," he said. "But there they are —the good old Shinies, and I'm glad to see them."

All that day, and day after day, the Rocky Mountains grew bigger and bigger. Kit could hardly take his eyes off them. Shining in the heat of the noonday sun, or breathing softly like sleeping giants under the moon—they were as thrilling as he'd dreamed they would be.

By the time they turned south from the Arkansas River, Pikes Peak was towering five thousand feet straight over their heads.

South across the hard, bare knees of the mountains rattled the wagon train. At the Pecos River, they turned west again and came to the valley of the Santa Fe. No need to urge on the mules now. They knew they were near the end of the trail. Riders came streaming down the valley to meet them.

Kit watched the gaily dressed Mexicans eagerly. They rode lively horses. Silver on their saddles and bridles glinted in the sun as they turned and led the way toward Santa Fe.

Soon the little town came in sight. It was snuggled up against the mountains at the head of the valley. The houses were flat, made of mud bricks. But the walls were very thick. In summer they were cool, and in winter, warm.

The whole town came out to meet the Americans. Shouts of welcome stirred the sunny air. The mules of the wagon train brayed. Little Mexican burros loaded down with firewood answered them cockily.

The mules pulled into the big square, or plaza. The long journey was over.

Kit looked around. It was just as his brothers had told him. The Governor's Palace stretched along the north side of the plaza. The Church of Our Lady of Light was across from it. After a short rest, Bent ordered the wagons on. Brightly dressed Mexican girls with flashing dark eyes, Mexican men with big hats stood watching the wagon train pass.

[65]

The whole town came out to meet the Americans

Just outside of town the wagon train stopped and the Americans made camp. The men unhitched their mules and got a quick supper. They were in a hurry. The town was waiting to celebrate their arrival.

"Payday!"

That was old Kincaid yelling. He put an iron box on the tail gate of a wagon and unlocked it. Charles Bent came and stood beside him with a tally book in his hands. The men lined up for their pay.

Kit was sitting by the fire, slowly finishing his supper. He didn't figure he'd get any pay. After all, he was a runaway. Captain Bent had done him a favor in bringing him along.

But when the last wagon man was paid, Bent looked around. He saw Kit and beckoned.

"What you going to do now, lad?" he asked.

Before Kit could answer, Kincaid spoke up. "Kit and me's goin' to Taos," he said.

"That's a trapper town," Bent said. "Are you going to be a trapper, Kit?"

"I hope so," Kit told him. "I aim to try."

"It's a hard life," Bent said. "But if a man's made for the mountains you can't keep him out of 'em. . . . Well, you'll need a little cash

[*67*]

till you get a job. Here's ten dollars. Keep your blankets and tin cup."

"Thanks," Kit said. "I'm sure grateful to you, Captain Bent."

"It's all right," said Bent. "I've got a lot of hope tied up in you, boy."

Kit's eyes sparkled with pleasure.

Before long he and Kincaid were on their way to Taos, nearly eighty miles to the north. It was autumn. The mountain tops were white with snow. Moss-green sage blanketed the valley. The air was clear and cool and the weather was perfect for their journey.

As they neared the little Mexican town, two long days later, Kit stared curiously at the whitewashed wall which surrounded it. He pulled his pony in to let Kincaid ride up beside him.

"Do you really reckon I'll get a job in this here town?" he asked. "A trapping job, I mean."

"If you want it bad enough, you will," Kincaid drawled. He dug his heels into his horse and rode ahead. Within half an hour he and Kit were clattering down a narrow street into the dusty plaza of Taos.

[68]

CHAPTER EIGHT

"Give 'Em Green River!"

WITH one hand on his long rifle, Kit leaned against a mud house, watching two Indian children who were playing in the dust. His stomach was empty, and he had no money to spend on food.

Three years had passed since he and Kincaid had come to Taos. Kincaid had died before the first winter ended. And Kit had not yet been able to get a job with a good band of trappers. Each time he had tried, he had been told that he was too young or too small.

"Why, a puny little runt like you couldn't even set a trap," one man had told him.

So Kit had earned his living mending saddles, driving teams for wagoners, and doing other odd jobs. Now he had had no work for some time, and he was broke and hungry.

"I got nothing I can sell, either, but this old rifle," he thought. "Maybe someone in the American House will give me a few dollars for it."

Shouldering his rusty flintlock, he went down the winding street. Then he crossed the little plaza and stepped into the only hotel in Taos.

The big central room was filled with mountain men. Ewing Young, who was captain of several bands of trappers, was pacing up and down the floor in a rage.

"We'll get beaver," he shouted as Kit came through the door, "and all the Injuns in the world won't stop us. We'll—"

"What's wrong?" Kit asked a shaggy-headed trapper who stood near the door.

"Plenty," the trapper replied gruffly. "We was trapping beaver on the Gila River, and those pesky Apaches attacked us. They drove us back to Taos, and Young's fit to be tied. He's hiring every man he can get who's got nerve enough to go out and fight them."

"Hiring men!" Kit didn't wait a minute. He stepped in front of Ewing Young and grounded his rifle.

[70]

"How about me going with you?" he asked.

"Can you hit anything with that old flint-lock?" Young roared.

"Sometimes," Kit said with a grin.

"They better be the right times," Young told him. "All right. Come along. I doubt anyone your size will ever make a mountain man or an Injun fighter, but we'll give you a try. Get Jim Higgins to give you a Green River knife and fix you up with an outfit."

Jim Higgins gave Kit what he needed. And next morning, just as the sun rose, the new band of forty fighting trappers started out for Indian country.

Some wore hooded coats. Some wore buckskins with fringes and designs of colored porcupine quills. All but Kit had fine Hawkens rifles. All carried deadly Green River knives with thick backs and sharp edges.

Kit rode proudly along on a blue-roan pony. The early mountain morning was cold. The boy was glad he had plenty of warm clothes. His blue wool shirt was covered with a long fringed buckskin coat. On his sandy head was a round wool hat.

His new knife hung from his belt along with

a whetstone and a bullet pouch. His powder-horn was slung over his shoulder and his old rifle rested in front of him on the saddle.

Behind him he led a string of pack mules tied head to tail. The traps which hung on their sawbuck packsaddles clinked cheerfully

in the crisp air. Kit was proud of his new outfit, and proud to be riding at last with the
mountain men.

Young and his men rode south and west
over the desert. A few days later they made
camp on the banks of a swift-flowing river.

Kit was hungry enough to eat an iron dog, but all he got was a snack of dried buffalo meat. The men were getting ready to set some traps in the river before dark. Kit was helping Captain Young unpack the mules. Young was going to give him his first lesson in trapping beaver.

Beside them was Jim Higgins. Kit noticed that Jim had stopped working and was gazing at a bare ridge above camp. A few seconds later Higgins touched Young's elbow and pointed to the ridge top.

Kit followed the line of his finger with his eyes. A head with a band of white cloth around the forehead showed beside a rock. Another head showed—and another. Why, the ridge top was alive with them!

Kit felt his spine tingle and his stomach go thin.

"Apaches!" Higgins said quietly. "Likely they're the same rascals that fought us before."

"There must be fifty of them," Young said. "If they surround us, they'll cut us up. We've got to trick them."

The camp was in a lightly wooded spot. The Indians were about two hundred yards away.

Young knew that they could not see very clearly what was going on among the trees.

He picked a dozen of his steadiest men. "You boys stay with me," he said. "We'll invite those pesky redskins into camp and give 'em a party. The rest of you fellows hide out. Hold your fire. But when I raise my left hand —give 'em Green River!"

To a mountain man, Green River meant war to the hilt. It came from the G. R., or Green River, the trade name that was stamped just below the hilt of their knives.

The twelve picked men stayed where they were. One by one the rest disappeared—behind rocks, behind trees, in clumps of bushes. Kit lay down behind two pack bags at the edge of camp. He covered himself with a buffalo robe and peered out between the bags.

Now the Indians were standing on the ridge top. They started walking cautiously downhill. Young shouted to them and motioned with his arm inviting them to come into the camp.

From his hiding place Kit watched the Indians walk toward the camp. They were naked except for their breech clouts, the cloth bands around their short black hair, and their yellow moccasins. Their brown bodies were lean and strong.

Kit heard Higgins say to Young, "Pretty cocky, ain't they?"

"They licked us before. That makes 'em brave," Young guessed.

"They're getting mighty careless," Higgins added. "Or maybe they're pulling the same trick we are."

"I don't think so," Young said. "They just want to look us over before they start a fight."

Kit was tense and excited. He could hear his heart beat. But he wasn't exactly afraid.

He watched the Apaches come into camp. When they found only a dozen men there, the Indians lost all caution. They began to tear open the packs. Kit wondered why Young didn't signal. The boy kept his rifle aimed at the chest of one big warrior.

Suddenly Young shot his left hand into the air. His right lifted his pistol from his belt.

Kit held his breath and gently tightened his finger on the trigger. He held without flinching, aiming at the tall Apache. The roar of his gun blended with many others. He saw the

Apache stagger and topple to the ground. It was Kit's first Indian—but just one more for his father's old rifle.

"Give 'em Green River!"

The old war cry rang out as the mountain men rose to their feet. The Indians were running in every direction.

By the time Young's men had reloaded, they were disappearing behind the ridge top. But fifteen Apaches lay dead on the ground.

As Kit looked at their twisted bodies, he felt a little sick. He wasn't glad that he had killed a man. Killing was part of the life he had chosen. He would have to kill many times again. But Kit Carson knew there was no sense in it.

Later he grew to know the Indians well. He liked and respected them, as they did him. He did what he could to prevent wars between them and the white men.

Now he turned away with a shudder as some of the men began to carry the bodies of the dead Apaches out of camp.

Later that evening, as the men sat around the campfire, Captain Young spoke across to him.

He aimed at the tall Apache

"Never turned a hair, did you, Kit?"

"I was too scared to notice," Kit answered.

Young laughed. "Maybe we'll make a mountain man of you yet, youngster."

Kit felt a warm glow. These were words he'd waited a long time to hear.

Young reached into the pack bag he had been leaning against. He dug out a small box and took something from it.

"Here, Kit," he said, and tossed the object across the fire.

Kit picked it up. It was a flat-headed brass tack. The boy knew what that meant. With the handle of his Green River knife he hammered the tack into the stock of his father's rifle.

That was the trappers' way of keeping count of the enemies they had killed.

CHAPTER NINE

Mountain Man

KIT CARSON became an expert trapper. Ewing Young taught him all he knew about where to look for beaver and how to catch them. Kit was always quick to learn. Soon he became Young's right-hand man.

The mountain men trapped and hunted through wild country far to the north and west of Taos. They trapped along the Arkansas River, which was the boundary between the United States and land belonging to Mexico. And along the swift-flowing Colorado. And down the Salt River, and up the Sacramento in the Mexican province of California.

Between trips, the trappers returned to Taos. One morning Kit went into the American House to see if Young had made plans for

[*80*]

another trip. Young had nothing for him to do at the moment. But another man was there, hiring trappers.

Kit knew him at once. Muscles bulged under the man's buckskin shirt. Red cheeks showed above his full black beard. He was making entries in an account book, and talking to Young.

As Kit walked toward him, Young said, "Now here's a likely lad for you, Fitz. He makes the beaver come and the Injuns go."

Tom Fitzpatrick looked up from his writing. His keen eyes looked over Kit's short, wiry figure. He smiled.

"Well, Kit," he said. "Been choking any saddlers lately?"

"One's enough," Kit answered with a grin. "How's chances to go trapping with you?"

"I think we can fix it," Fitz replied. "I've been hoping you and I would get together again some time."

Kit let out a war whoop and began to dance in circles. For once, the usually quiet young man showed his excitement.

"If Fitz will hire me, I'm a real mountain man—and no mistake," he thought happily.

Tom Fitzpatrick and four other men had started the Rocky Mountain Fur Company. Soon after Kit joined them, Fitz headed north with a band of mountain men.

One bright autumn afternoon Kit was riding up the Salmon River valley in what is now the State of Idaho, looking for beaver sign. Ahead of him, through the leafless aspen trees, he could see the snow-topped Bitter Root Mountains.

Things had gone well with him ever since he had started to work for Fitzpatrick. Already he had caught so many beaver that, in the trappers' winter camp, he had two packs of skins. They were worth about a thousand dollars and some day they would be made into men's hats. But Kit was not thinking of this as he rode up the valley. He was thinking of the work he had to do.

He squinted up at the dazzling peaks, and then let his eyes fall to the lower slopes. They were already in shadow.

"Better find beaver quick, old hoss," he said to his chunky blue roan, "or we won't get back to camp tonight."

He glanced behind at the round-bellied,

[*82*]

black pack mule that had stopped to nibble at the tips of a red willow bush. Mules don't like to be lonesome any more than men. He knew the beast would follow.

Kit kept a close lookout toward the river as he heeled his blue roan to a faster gait. Presently he saw a flash of white at the bottom of a young cottonwood tree. As he rode near he saw that a beaver had gnawed all around the bottom of the trunk.

The pack mule had come up and was eating the cottonwood gnawings around the foot of the tree. Kit led him and the roan into a willow thicket and tied them.

He took his sack of six traps off the pack mule and walked through thick brush toward the river. As he parted the last screen of bushes, there lay before him a quiet beaver pond. The beaver had heard him come and were hiding in their lodges.

He looked and listened intently for any sign of Indian or rival trapper.

Then he set a trap at the foot of a slide where the beaver went in and out of the river. He tied a float stick to the trap chain. If a beaver was caught, and pulled the trap into

The beaver were hiding in their lodges

deep water, the float stick would show Kit where it was.

Kit set the rest of his traps. Afterwards, he was careful to splash water over his tracks. Even a little scent of man might make the beaver wary.

As Kit made his way back to his horse and mule he thought, "If I'm lucky, I'll get six prime furs in the morning. That'll be thirty-six dollars for my day's work."

Kit headed back for camp. This was the time of year for game to be fat. He thought a juicy elk steak would taste good for supper. He kept his eyes open.

Sure enough. His eye caught movement in a clump of brush about two hundred yards away. Looking closely, he could make out a set of big antlers.

He dismounted quietly and tied up his horse and pack mule. Making no noise, he started on foot to stalk the elk.

He was up wind from the elk so it couldn't smell him. Soon it came walking easily into the open, snatching mouthfuls of brush as it went. It was a tall, eight-point buck, fat and sassy.

Kit lay down behind a fallen log and drew a careful bead just behind the elk's shoulder. He squeezed trigger. The rifle barked. The elk lurched forward and sank to the ground.

Suddenly Kit heard a coughing grunt behind him, then a rushing sound. He turned and leaped to his feet. Two huge grizzly bears were lumbering toward him, their teeth bared.

CHAPTER TEN

A Tiff with Grizzlies

THERE was no time to reload and no use to shoot if there had been. The grizzly bear is the toughest thing going. He can run a mile with enough bullets in him to bring a bull buffalo plunging to earth. Only a dead center shot to the brain will kill him. And Kit knew that if he killed one bear, the other would get him.

Dropping his rifle, Kit turned and ran. The bears ran after him. There were no good climbing trees near by, but Kit made for the best, grabbed a branch, and swung up.

Out of the corner of his eye he saw the bigger bear rear up on his hind legs and raise a mighty forepaw with bared claws. Kit drew up his legs till his stomach muscles cramped. The claws slashed out.

He saw the bigger bear rear up on his hind legs

Kit felt them catch his moccasin. It ripped and came off. The young trapper climbed higher up the slippery trunk. He grabbed the next branch and pulled himself up farther. Trembling, sweating, and gasping for breath, he rested.

The bears snarled and bit and clawed at the tree. The tree was too small for Kit to get far out of reach. He knew that the grizzly is no great tree climber like the black and brown bears. But he can climb some. If this one got very far up the tree, it would be the end of Kit.

"I won't be the first trapper that ever cashed in his beaver on account of bears," Kit thought grimly.

But he didn't have much time to worry about it. The larger beast dug his hind claws into the base of the tree, and started scrambling up. He put a front paw over the first branch. Kit got out his Green River knife and started hacking at a two-inch branch above his head.

The bear paused a second, eyeing him. Then he came on. Kit pulled at the partly cut branch with all his strength. It broke. He chopped off a length. Grasping it firmly in his right hand, he hung on tightly to a limb above him with his left.

His heart thudded as he looked down into a wide-open red mouth with huge white teeth. The great jaws snapped at his foot. Kit leaned over and whacked the bear's nose hard with the branch.

The bear snarled and lunged again. Again Kit struck—again and again. The bear began to back down snarling. He was so angry when he reached the ground that he started tearing up the roots of the tree.

The elk which Kit had shot was not very far away. The smaller bear kept sniffing as if it smelled something. Kit hoped it was the blood of the elk. It might lure both bears away.

But the bear with the hurt nose went right on digging roots, growling and snarling as hard as ever. The tree began to sway. Kit took a firmer grasp on his knife. If the tree went over, he'd at least make a fight of it.

Suddenly a stronger breeze blew over the elk. The smaller bear trotted over toward it and began to eat. The other bear turned and watched. He looked back at Kit and then again at the elk. Plainly he, too, wanted some of that meat. Once more he looked up in the tree. Then he gave one last growl and made for the elk.

Kit waited half a minute. He made sure the grizzlies' minds were on their meal. Then he climbed down the tree. His legs trembled as he sneaked away. He grabbed up his rifle and ran for his horse and mule. Yanking loose their tie ropes, he hopped aboard the horse and rode quickly down the valley. Before long he was in sight of the trappers' camp.

As Kit approached, he could see the camp-fire flickering against the cliffs, and the three-sided lodge where the men lived. This was made of poles with buffalo hides stretched over them. It was rounded like a cave. The front side faced the cliff and was open to the fire. The cliff threw back the heat.

The trappers had picked a sheltered valley for their winter quarters. They had camped in the part of the valley which faced south. When snow fell, they knew that the sun would some-times melt it down to grass. Buffalo would come there to winter. And antelope, deer, and elk would not be far away.

The camp looked good to Kit as he rode in

that night. Strips of buffalo meat were drying on a frame over a low smoky fire.

The trappers had already eaten and were sitting at the edge of the lodge in front of the fire, swapping yarns. Kit felt a warm glow of friendship as he counted them. He was the last man in.

Kit turned loose his horse and mule and hung up his traps on poles inside the lodge.

Then he came out to the fire. He grabbed a hot hump rib of buffalo. Filling his tin cup with steaming coffee, he settled down to eat.

The trappers ate almost nothing but meat. It kept them strong and healthy, but they needed a lot of it. Eight pounds of buffalo meat a day were just about enough to keep a husky trapper fit.

When he finished eating, Kit settled back on a buffalo robe, and lit his clay pipe. Full of good hump meat and warmed by the fire, he was happy. This was the life he loved. And now was storytelling time. The trappers made up their own stories. And they were good at it.

"How come you're so late getting in?" Fitz asked Kit.

Kit told his tale of the bears. Most of the

The trappers were sitting by the fire, swapping yarns

trappers burst into loud guffaws. It was a good story, they said. But they either didn't believe him, or pretended not to.

Jim Bridger, the greatest storyteller of them all, was the only one who didn't laugh.

"Well, now, boys," he said, "that could happen, you know. I've seen lots stranger things than that in these mountains."

"We know that, Jim," Tom Fitzpatrick said sarcastically. "Some of the things you've seen would take the bark off an old cottonwood tree."

Jim had been one of the first white men to see the great geysers of Yellowstone Park. Whenever he had told his friends about columns of steam and hot water shooting high in the air from the ground, they had called him the biggest liar in the West. He soon grew tired of this and began to make up real whoppers just to get even.

Now Jim Bridger said, "I don't reckon any of you new men ever run into the glass mountain that lays to the north of here, did you?"

Jolly Joe Meek jumped to his feet. "Wait a minute, Jim, before you start that one."

Joe cupped his hands around his mouth

[*94*]

and yelled at the top of his voice, *"Time to get up!"*

Joe was a rogue; always up to something. He'd been in the mountains longer than Kit, though he was a year younger.

He and Kit were opposites. Kit took life in earnest. To Joe Meek it was all in fun. But the two were good friends.

"What's that for?" Kit asked.

"Why, Kit," Joe answered seriously, "that glass mountain Jim is fixing to tell you about has a funny echo. If you holler before you go to bed, the echo gets back just in time to wake you up in the morning."

Bill Mitchell snorted.

Scrawny Bill Williams let his chin drop on his chest and began to snore. These yarns were all old to him.

But Kit was all ears.

"What about it, Jim?" he asked. "What about the glass mountain?"

"You mean what about it besides the echo?" Jim Bridger asked. "Ain't that enough?"

"Is it a big mountain?"

"Well, Kit," Jim drawled, "it's hard to tell just how big it is. No one's ever seen it."

[*95*]

"Then how do they know it's there?"

"Why, that's easy, son. There's the bones of birds piled up at the foot of it twenty feet high. They've flown into it so hard they were killed."

"Have you ever touched it, Jim? Ever tried to climb it?"

"That I have, son. I found out the hard way. It's too slippery to climb. . . . One time I was being chased by Blackfoot Injuns. I was on a fast horse, something like that blue roan of yours. He was going like an old jack rabbit and gaining on them Injuns every jump.

"Well, sir, we came to that big pile of bird bones. Now that horse was one of the best jumpers west of Missouri. He hunched up his hindquarters and took off. He would have gone plumb over that twenty-foot pile o' bones. But he hit his head on the glass mountain and fell down dead.

"I went right over the saddle and bumped my head on the glass too. That glass is so clear I still couldn't see it. But I could tell by the bump on my head it must be there.

"So I tried to climb it. But I slipped down faster than I went up. By this time the Injuns had caught up and the arrows were bouncing off that glass as thick as cat fur. I went for my rifle, but it was stuck under my horse and I couldn't get it out."

Jim Bridger stopped talking. He reached into his pocket for his tobacco pouch. Slowly he filled his pipe.

All the trappers' eyes were shining in the light of the campfire, Kit's especially. He didn't dare speak for fear Jim would refuse to tell the ending.

Jim Bridger pulled a coal out of the fire with a pair of crossed sticks. He lit his clay pipe and started puffing away contentedly. Then Kit could hold in no longer.

"What happened then, Jim?" he asked. "How did you get away?"

"Why, Kit," Bridger said. "I didn't. That was the time the Blackfoot Injuns killed me."

There was a great roar of laughter and slapping of legs around the campfire. Kit joined with the rest.

He stood up and stretched.

"Guess I'd better turn in," he said, yawning, "if I want to get to sleep before that echo comes back."

"You're right," Jim said. "And if that echo don't convince you," he added, "you just ride out there in the morning and climb that pile of bones. You'll find mine and the jumper's somewheres near the top."

CHAPTER ELEVEN

Little Chief

THE winter passed quickly. When spring came, Tom Fitzpatrick went east with a wagon train to St. Louis. Kit took a job with a trapper named Gant.

For months all went well. They trapped for beaver and hunted buffalo in country where the Arapaho Indians lived, along the Arkansas River. Then Gant began to trade with the Indians for buffalo robes. One day Kit found out that Gant was cheating the Arapahoes. In great disgust he packed up his belongings and left.

He had heard that his old friend, Captain Charles Bent, was building a huge fort and trading post not far away. So he rode downriver to see what was going on.

The walls of the fort were almost finished.
They enclosed a big space one hundred and
fifty feet long and a hundred feet wide. Kit
rode through an opening which was to be one
of the doors. Just beyond it, he saw Charles
Bent bossing a gang of workmen.

Kit went over to him.

"Haugh, Charlie," he said, pulling up his
horse.

"Kit!" Bent exclaimed. "Long time no see."

"I'm looking for work, Charlie," Kit said,
swinging himself from his saddle. "I got sick
of Gant."

"Don't blame you," Bent drawled. "Well,
you've come to the right place. We're about
through with the walls. But I need logs bad to
make the buildings inside. How about you
taking a gang out and cutting some?"

"Suits me," replied Kit. "Have you got any
men who can swing an axe?"

"You bet," Bent said. "The best in the
world."

Next morning Kit and the logging outfit set
out for Horse Creek, where there was plenty
of good timber.

There were a dozen strong men in the party,

who sang and joked as they rode along. They'd
come west to trap, but they didn't mind
logging for a change. Their leader was big
Jacques le Boeuf.

They had a wagon with them, filled with
axes, saws, and canthooks for rolling the logs.
Handling the reins over the four mules was a
man named Joe Blaine.

Kit rode beside the wagon on a tall horse.
He had brought along plenty of rifles, powder,
and bullets.

Jacques le Boeuf reached into the wagon,

[*101*]

picked up a rifle, and waved it. "What is this, a war?" he shouted. "Hey, I hired out to chop, not fight."

Kit laughed. "You like that thick head of black hair, don't you?" he asked.

"It keeps me warm," Jacques joked.

"Well," Kit told him. "We're not hunting trouble. But we're going into Injun country."

It wasn't far to Horse Creek. When they reached there they began at once to build a cabin, a corral, and a lean-to stable.

While his men were at this work, Kit went hunting. Shortly they were snug and warm and had a good supply of buffalo meat.

Then they began to cut timber. Logs piled up quickly. On Kit's orders, the men kept their rifles with them when they worked. But for a long time there was no sign of Indians.

The men had turned their horses and mules loose to graze. When grass grew scarce near by, the animals wandered farther and farther away from camp. But they came in to the corral each night and morning for grain. Then they had to be turned loose again to find grass. Kit figured he couldn't spare any men to guard them.

One day two friendly Cheyenne Indians came riding toward the camp. They told Kit that their names were Little Turtle and Black Whiteman. They said they were on the way to Bent's Fort to trade. Kit invited them to tie their horses in the stable and to spend the night.

Next morning Joe Blaine went out to the corral to feed grain to the stock as usual. In no time at all he was back in the cabin. "Stock's gone!" he announced.

"What's that?" Kit said sharply.

"Stock's gone," Joe repeated. "The animals didn't come in to the corral this morning. There's two inches of snow on the ground, and not a track."

"That can't mean but one thing," Kit said. "Injuns got 'em. And we're plumb afoot." He looked at the tall, handsome Cheyennes. "You're better trailers than we are," he said. "How about taking a look?"

Little Turtle said, "We go see."

Mounting their horses, he and Black Whiteman set out. In half an hour they were back. Speaking slowly, they said that a bunch of Crow Indians had stolen all the stock.

[*103*]

Kit made up his mind quickly, as usual.

"We can't let them get away with this," he said. "We'll go after 'em."

"What, on foot?" Joe Blaine asked.

"By gum, we'll go on our hands if we have to," Kit told him.

"We help," Little Turtle said.

Kit turned to his men. "Get your guns and make sure you got plenty of powder and bullets," he ordered. By the time Kit's men were ready, the Cheyennes had set out alone to overtake the Crows.

On the snow-covered ground the trail was easy to follow. The tracks of the ponies of Little Turtle and Black Whiteman led into the broad trail which the Crows had left as they traveled with the stolen horses.

Kit and his men hiked slowly over the prairie.

"Ain't it kind of crazy," Joe Blaine asked, "to go walking after men who are riding?"

"Never can tell," Kit told him. "Sometimes a man afoot will out-travel a horse. It takes horses a long time to eat enough grass to keep going. And they tire mighty fast if they don't get anything to eat."

[104]

It was noon when they caught sight of the two Cheyennes outlined sharply against the skyline ahead. All afternoon the tiring loggers plodded along, keeping their Indian guides in sight.

The sun was getting low when the weary trailers saw a thicket a quarter of a mile away, over the white stretch of snow. Suddenly a little shower of sparks shot out of the black tangle of wild plum bushes.

Kit stopped his men. Little Turtle and Black Whiteman came riding back to pow-wow with Kit. In a minute the two Indians rode off to one side and disappeared into a gully that led toward the thicket.

"Spread out, boys," Kit ordered. "Keep in line. And keep your rifles ready."

Slowly he and his men walked across the snow.

From the thicket came the shrill yapping of a dog. Then a puff of steam shot up.

"Tough luck," Kit thought. "The dog warned 'em, and they threw snow on their fire."

He quickened his step. His men kept pace. They neared the thicket. Suddenly sixty Crow

They gave the Indians a dose of hot lead

Indians charged out at them with wild war cries.

Kit and his men ran for their lives. They were afraid they'd be surrounded. But when they reached a little ridge, they dropped behind it. They aimed their rifles and gave the Crows a dose of hot lead.

Two Indians dropped. The rest ran back into the thicket to get their horses. But they found not hoof, hide, nor hair! Kit's Cheyenne friends had run off every last one.

"Give 'em Green River, boys!" Kit shouted.

The dozen loggers rushed the thicket. The two Cheyennes began to shoot from cover to one side. The Crows didn't want to lose any more men. They ran through the thicket and scattered over the prairie beyond.

Kit felt a surge of relief.

"Our luck's good so far," he said, "let's not push it."

His tired men had no desire to chase the Crows. They went back to the next patch of woods, where the Cheyennes had driven the horses, and made camp for the night.

Kit's active mind as usual worked over the day's lessons.

Chief Yellow Wolf had come to the fort to trade

"It's been a tough day," he told the men, "but I reckon I learned something."

"I learned I never should've come West," Joe Blaine joked. "What did you learn, Kit?"

Kit answered, "Don't ever let your stock run loose at night without a guard. I never thought those Crows would be a thousand miles from home in winter. But they were."

Next morning Turtle and Whiteman rode out to the plum thicket. They found two dead Crows. When they got back they made fun of the loggers. Thirteen shots and only two dead men.

But Kit knew his gun had killed one of the Crows. He put a fourth brass tack in the stock of his rifle, and figured it was nothing to be ashamed of.

The Cheyennes, in spite of their joking, agreed with him. Later that month Kit went into Bent's Fort for supplies. Chief Yellow Wolf, of the Cheyennes, and some of his band were there. They had come to the fort to trade.

Yellow Wolf was sitting on a bale of furs. He was wrapped in a buffalo robe. White men and red were all around him.

When Kit came into the fort, Yellow Wolf

[*110*]

stood up. He held his chief's pipe along his left forearm. Waving his right hand, he made a little speech. He spoke in a mixture of Cheyenne and sign language. But Kit understood enough to know what he was talking about.

At the end Yellow Wolf said, "The white man is young. He is small. His hair is short and thin. But he is brave."

Then the wise old chief turned to Kit. "My son," he went on, "I give you a new name. You have won it. From where the sun now stands, your name is Vih'hui-nis, Little Chief."

Even today when the Cheyennes speak of Kit Carson they call him "Little Chief."

CHAPTER TWELVE

The Carson Men

BEFORE long Kit had more than an Indian name. He had an Indian wife. She was a pretty girl from the Arapaho tribe named Grass Singing.

Grass Singing went on trapping expeditions with Kit. She kept his tepee neat and made his buckskin clothes and moccasins. She cured his beaver skins so well that they brought high prices.

Kit made plenty of money and bought her everything she wanted. They were very happy together. When their baby girl was born, Kit named her Adeline, and thought she was the prettiest baby in the world.

By that time Kit had become the captain of a band of mountain men. They trapped along the Yellowstone River, the Bighorn, and the Snake. Beaver were plentiful. But in the summer of 1838, bad luck came.

Hat makers in the East began to make silk hats instead of beaver hats. The trappers couldn't get enough money for their beaver skins to buy supplies.

"One dollar for each skin! That's all a man can get now. One dirty little dollar," complained one of the trappers as the men sat around their campfire.

"And only last year we got six for a prime skin," drawled old Bill Williams. "Eight dollars, if it was squaw-cured."

Kit Carson stood up. "Looks like the beaver trade's done for, all right," he said. "I aim to make tracks for Bent's Fort tomorrow. I reckon Charlie Bent will help us."

Turning on his heel, he went into his tepee to tell Grass Singing to get ready to move. Next morning he and his men were up before daylight. By the time the sun rose, they were riding south toward Bent's Fort on the Arkansas River.

It was a gloomy band of trappers that Kit led out of the mountains several days later.

The men rode along in silence, still unable to believe that their good beaver trade had ended.

Suddenly Kit turned in his saddle. "Cheer up, boys," he said. "I'll bet my Sunday saddle against an old beaver tail that we'll do better working for Bent than we did wading around ice-cold creeks. And there's the fort. Ain't that something?" He stopped his horse and pointed.

They had rounded a bend in the mountain trail. A great plain stretched out before them to the horizon. And at the foot of the trail lay Bent's Fort.

Grass Singing pulled her horse close to Kit's. Strapped to her back, on a baby board, was little Adeline. While her parents looked ahead over the plain, Adeline gazed peacefully back at the huge jumble of mountains behind them.

Grass Singing had never seen the fort before. As they drew nearer, she stared at the high reddish adobe walls and the two round towers which had loopholes through which cannon and rifles could be fired. But she looked longest at the two huge doors in the center wall. Thousands of brass nails had been

At the foot of the trail lay Bent's Fort

pounded into each one of those wooden doors, so that no enemy could set the doors afire. The nails flashed back the sunlight so brightly that she could barely see the lookout tower above the doors, with its telescope and bell.

But Kit had touched heel to his horse and was riding rapidly ahead. Grass Singing and the trappers followed him.

The great nail-studded doors were open when they reached the fort. Captain Bent was standing there to meet them. He gave Kit a hearty handshake.

"Light right down and rest your saddle," he said. "I'm mighty glad to see you."

Swinging himself from his saddle, Kit handed his reins to one of the men and followed Bent into the fort. Grass Singing dismounted and began to unpack the tepee. The others rode around to the corral behind the fort to put up their horses.

The Bent brothers were now doing business with Indians and white people for a thousand miles in every direction. Their fort was a tremendous place. Inside, it looked almost like a small town. More than a hundred men lived there—blacksmiths, clerks, packers, teamsters, hunters, traders, laborers, and a doctor. Many of these men had their wives and children living with them.

In the center of the fort was a great fur press. Kit and Bent sat down at its foot and stoked their pipes. Kit came right to the point.

"Beaver's done for, Charlie," he said. "What do we do now?"

"I'd be plumb tickled if you'd go to work for me," Bent said without hesitation.

Kit's clear gray eyes twinkled. He smiled under his sandy mustache.

"I rode five hundred miles to hear you say that," he remarked. "How do I fit in?"

"Two ways, Kit," Bent said. "First, with some three hundred mouths to feed, we need lots of meat. Sometimes we don't get enough. You can get real hunters. I want you to organize two buffalo hunts a year, dry the meat, and bring it in.

"Besides the meat, the robe business is growing all the time. We may soon sell more buffalo robes than we do beaver skins."

"I reckon I can get the meat and robes all right for you," Kit said.

"I know you can," Bent agreed. "My second

problem is guarding wagon trains between here and Missouri. Raids by Indians are costing me plenty."

"You're laying me out a big job of work," Kit said with a smile.

"You can do it," Bent said. "You're a natural leader. You'll need about fifty men, Kit. I reckon you won't have any trouble rounding them up."

Kit had no trouble at all.

"Carson's hiring hunters!" The word spread quickly throughout the West. Men came pouring out of their camps in the mountains. Down from the Snake River, the Salmon, the Powder, and the Bear. Clear from California!

"Beaver's done! Carson's hiring buffalo hunters. Want to work for Kit Carson? Now there's a man to tie to!"

Kit could pick and choose from the men who came flocking to the fort. It wasn't long before he had an outfit that could ride the rough spots.

One bright September morning they all set out from Bent's Fort on their first big hunt. Each hunter was mounted and led an extra horse which had been especially trained for

[*118*]

buffalo hunting. In addition to the hunters there were cavvy drivers, camp tenders, and pack mules galore.

They headed northeast. Slowly a great red sun wheeled up in the sky and poured its warmth over the high plains.

When they reached Smoky Hill River they met a band of Kiowa Indians. A young Kiowa chief named Stumbling Bear came toward them with his hand outstretched. He held the palm of his hand forward, as a sign of friendship.

"Haugh," he said, halting before the hunters.

"Haugh, Bear," replied Kit.

Stumbling Bear gave the Indian sign for buffalo. He made Kit understand that he and the other Kiowas wanted to join Kit's outfit. The Indians were fine hunters and Kit was glad to have them come along.

Together they all crossed a ridge and traveled down toward the Republican River. On the morning of the third day, Kit saw Stumbling Bear give a signal from a rounded hilltop, which meant, "Buffalo ahead."

Spurring his horse, Kit joined the young

chief on the hill. Half a mile away the plains were black with buffalo. Kit thought that there must be a thousand of the great beasts. They were grazing south, almost directly toward him.

He plucked a handful of dry grass and tossed it into the air. It drifted straight toward the herd.

The buffalo does not see or hear well, but his nose is very keen. Kit knew that if the herd got a whiff of the hunters, they'd gallop away with the roar of a sudden thunderstorm.

[*120*]

He and Stumbling Bear rode back to the hunters. Kit told the Kiowas to ride around behind the herd and to hem the animals in down either side, as far as they could. He and his men would close in from the front.

The Indians rode off, upwind, and Kit spread his men out in a long line. Soon he could see Indian riders taking their places behind and around the great herd.

Suddenly the Kiowas broke into wild hunting cries. The shaggy buffalo began to bellow and move about restlessly. Those in the rear started to run forward. They pushed in on the ones in front. The herd closed up like a big brown accordion. Kiowa riders pinched it in from the sides.

Kit's tall, thin buffalo horse was as tense as a coiled spring. His nostrils were quivering with eagerness for the chase.

Kit's mouth was full of bullets, so he couldn't shout to his men. But he waved to them to go ahead.

"Ya-a-hoo!" The men pounded away toward the herd, yelling at the top of their lungs.

Kit let the reins slip through his fingers and his horse shot forward like an arrow from a bow. Kit took quick aim, fired, and the lead buffalo dropped to the ground. Hastily Kit loaded his rifle as his horse sped in front of the herd. Aiming, he fired again. Another buffalo stumbled and fell.

Along the line Kit's hunters were also firing and loading. Every time a fat cow went down the men yelled a wild cry of triumph. The front of the herd began to turn. The hunters were trying to get them to circle—to mill.

Suddenly Kit's horse stepped into a prairie-dog hole and turned a somersault. Kit shot from the saddle, went head over heels through the air, and landed right side up.

He picked up his rifle almost as he landed. His horse was already up and running away. The roaring herd was nearly on top of Kit. He was ready to grab a handful of brown wool

[123]

and jump on a buffalo's back if he could.

And then, swooping down like a barn swallow, came a hunter named Sol Silver on his big gray horse. His rifle was cradled in his right arm, along with his reins. He reached his left arm out toward Kit. Kit grabbed it and swung himself up behind Sol's saddle.

"Watch out!" Sol yelled, as a big bull buffalo hooked at Kit's leg.

The gray horse jumped away from the sharp horns. Kit clung on for dear life until they had reached the top of the hill. There the two men dismounted, and from a kneeling position, began again to shoot buffalo.

The herd was running now in a cloud of dust. The riders were forcing the buffalo to run in a circle. Before long the whole herd was going around and around. The plain was dotted with carcasses. Kit figured that they had killed enough buffalo to keep all his men busy cutting up meat until after dark. He signaled with his arm. The men stopped shooting and slowed down their horses.

In no time the remaining buffalo were grazing some distance away, as peacefully as if nothing had disturbed their morning meal.

The hunters dismounted from their horses and loosened their cinches.

"I guess we made them come," shouted a man named Bill Mitchell.

"It takes the Carson Men!" Sol Silver yelled back.

And so the name was born. The fame of the Carson Men spread far and wide. Soon it became the ambition of almost every man in the mountains to belong to Kit's band. And Kit became known as one of the finest leaders in the West.

CHAPTER THIRTEEN

The Wagon Train Fight

CAPTAIN KIT CARSON stood in the lookout tower of Bent's Fort. Below he could see his little daughter, Adeline, playing tag with a small Mexican boy. Adeline was five years old now, and as wild as an unbroken colt.

"She'd ought to be getting some book-learning soon," Kit thought. "She'd ought to have a woman to look after her, too. If her mother had lived—"

A lump rose suddenly in Kit's throat. Grass Singing had become ill while Kit was off on his first buffalo hunt for the fort. Soon after his return, she had died. Nearly three years had passed since then, but Kit still missed her.

With a sigh, he turned and looked east toward the Santa Fe Trail. There was a puff of dust away down the Arkansas River. Kit put his eye to the telescope. A rider showed up under the dust, galloping toward the fort. For a moment a dip in the trail hid him from sight. When he appeared again, Kit could see he was Sol Silver.

Sol was using whip and spurs on his weary black horse. He reached the fort and pulled his panting animal to a stop in a cloud of dust. Kit was already on the ground, waiting for him. Sol's horse was worn out. Sol slid from the saddle, wiping his face on his sleeve.

"Seventy miles, I rode!" he told Kit. "There's a big wagon train forted up, away down the river, Kit. Comanche Injuns are buzzing around it like flies. It's gone beaver unless we can get there to save it."

Kit didn't waste a minute. He cupped his hands to his mouth.

"*Carson Men!* Come a-running!" he shouted.

Some of his men were busy shoeing horses. Others were mending saddles, fixing guns, braiding rawhide ropes, pitching horseshoes. Whatever they were doing, they dropped it quickly and poured out from their quarters.

"Saddle up!" Kit called.

In no time the men were tearing for the corral with saddles over their shoulders and saddle blankets and bridles over their arms. They roped their horses, saddled them, and tightened cinches. Soon the band of fifty mountain men was ready to ride.

They streamed out of the corral behind their leader and pounded away down the Arkansas River. Sol Silver, on a fresh horse, was with them. Each man led a spare horse. And from each man's belt hung one of the new revolvers which had just been invented by a man named Samuel Colt.

The sun set and it grew dark as the men galloped east. They rode almost all night. Several miles before they reached the place where the wagon train was forted up, they went down into the dry riverbed. With Sol as their guide, they rode along the riverbed as quietly as they could.

It was still dark when they came to a flat place along the river, with a steep bank beyond it. They dismounted and Sol led them up to the edge of the bank. The men looked

[*128*]

over it and saw the huge square of a wagon train looming up in the starlight about a quarter of a mile away. Beyond the wagons was a line of hills.

Kit thought the Comanches were probably hiding in those hills. He didn't dare let his men ride right up to the camp.

"They'll have sentries posted," he said to his men in a low tone. "Like as not they'd mistake us for Injuns and shoot us clear out of our saddles. Tom Hill, can you get into the camp and let them know we're coming?"

"Count on me," Tom said. "I'll get in slick as snake oil."

He handed the reins of his horse to a friend. Climbing over the riverbank, he melted into the dark prairie. In half an hour, he was back.

"It's all right," he said. "I warned the wagon boss."

"Let's go, boys," Kit ordered quietly.

The fifty men swung into their saddles. They spurred their horses over the bank and made for the wagons at a high lope. Streaming into the corral, they dismounted.

Some of the wagoners were trying to sleep. Others stood about waiting uneasily for some-

[*129*]

thing to happen. The gaunt wagon master came forward and shook hands with Kit.

"I'm surely glad to see you," he said earnestly.

"How are you making out?" Kit asked.

"Right now," the captain said, "you wouldn't think there was an Injun in the world. But yesterday they were after us like hornets."

"Did you lose any men?"

"Yes, one dead, and two hurt."

Kit cast his eye over the mules and oxen that were held in the big corral. There must have been three hundred of them. They were wandering about, snatching hungrily at any bit of fodder that was left.

"They'd make quite a haul for the Comanches," Kit said.

"Yep! The Indians will do a lot of fighting to get them," the wagon master agreed. "Along about sundown last night we saw a big band of Kiowas ride in and join the Comanches. They all rode back of the hills at sundown. Now it's 'most sunup and I guess they're still there. They'll surely hit us again later this morning."

"I'm surely glad to see you," he said

Kit nodded and turned to his men.

"Boys," he said, "take your saddles off and put them in the wagons on that side." He pointed to the side of the square which faced the hills. "Then crawl into the wagons yourselves and keep quiet," he added. "When the Injuns come it's just possible that we can surprise them."

The men crawled into the wagons which were loaded with store goods and supplies. Quiet settled over the camp.

The rim of the sun was just showing when a line of naked Indians came riding over a ridge. The chiefs had on their war bonnets.

Kit watched the line flow out over the ridge top. He tried to count the Indians and then gave up. There were hundreds! Kit's men and the wagoners together came to less than one hundred.

Suddenly blood-chilling war cries sounded from the hill. Half the warriors came charging down toward the wagon train.

When they were within a hundred yards of the train, Kit said quietly, "Let 'em have it, boys."

His men had loosened the wagon covers on

[*132*]

the side toward the Indians. Now they stuck their rifles out under the covers. That side of the caravan became a blaze of fire. Smoke floated into the still morning air and drifted away.

Indians dropped from their horses. Ponies somersaulted. Some screamed. Some lay still.

Two Indians abreast galloped up to the dead and wounded, reached down and carried them off by their arms.

But then the second half of the Indian band came charging their bright paint horses down the hill. This was an old Indian trick. Half of them would attack and draw the fire. The other half would ride in for the kill before their victims could reload.

This time the charging Indians came within a hundred yards of the wagons. Shouting like a pack of wolves, the Comanche braves came nearer.

They rode within fifty yards—twenty-five. Then the Carson Men used their revolvers. Five shots rattled from each gun. Death cluttered the prairie.

The Indians wheeled their horses. The frightened animals needed no urging. They shot over the hilltop like jack rabbits in front of a pack of hounds. They didn't come back.

The Carson Men and the wagoners hopped down from the wagons. They wiped the gunpowder from their faces.

"I guess we surprised them all right," Kit said dryly.

"It looks that way," the wagon master agreed. He counted noses and found that none of his men had been hurt. "Do you think the

Injuns will come back again?" he asked Kit.
"You've seen the last of that bunch," Kit
told him. "Indians are pretty wise soldiers.
When they start losing men they quit. They
don't like a chief that brings home dead warriors."

"Is it all right for us to go on?" the wagon master asked.

"I think it is," Kit replied. "We'll guard you in to Bent's Fort."

The story of the wagon train fight was told from Missouri to the Pacific Ocean. That wasn't the only wagon train Kit and his men rescued. Soon travelers knew that wherever the Carson Men rode, the Santa Fe Trail was safe.

CHAPTER FOURTEEN

Two Sound Like Twenty

THE little steamboat chugged noisily up the Missouri River. Kit Carson walked along the narrow deck, watching the shores glide by. He had come east to St. Louis to put six-year-old Adeline in a boarding school. Now he was on his way west again and glad he was going.

"Cities ain't no place for this coot," Kit said to himself. "And when I get back—"

Kit smiled. He had fallen in love with a girl in Taos. She was a beautiful girl named Josefa and Kit planned to marry her as soon as he could. But he'd need to earn more money than Bent was paying him for hunting buffalo. Thinking of this, Kit leaned on the railing and stared across the water. A stranger stepped up and stood beside him.

"I understand you're a mountain man," the stranger said. "My name's Frémont. Lieutenant John Charles Frémont. I'm on my way west for the United States Government, and the man who was to guide my expedition didn't meet me in St. Louis as he promised. Do you know anyone who could take his place?"

"Maybe so," said Kit. "How far west are you going?"

"Into the Rocky Mountains. The Government wants me to explore the country, make maps of it, and find out if it's worth settling. But I must have a guide. Do you know the mountains?"

"Like I was born in them," Kit drawled. "I reckon I could take you most any place you'd want to go."

"Good!" said Frémont. He liked Kit and had already heard about him from people in St. Louis. "I'll pay you a hundred dollars a month," he added.

Kit looked pleased. The two men shook hands and the matter was settled.

Frémont's expedition set out from a trading post near the mouth of the Kansas River several days later. There were twenty-one men in his party. Most of them had horses and all were well armed. They took along eight carts loaded with tents and supplies.

For weeks Kit led them west, through wild mountain country. Each evening they stopped and wheeled their carts into a circle. Inside the circle they set up tents, built fires, and made camp for the night. Then Frémont made maps of the country through which they had traveled and wrote reports for the United States Government of what they had seen and done. In these reports he spoke often of his wonderful guide, Kit Carson.

At last Frémont and his party reached a gap in the mountains called South Pass. Soon after this, they turned back. When they reached Fort Laramie, Kit left them, since he was no longer needed. With money in his pockets he hurried home to Taos and married beautiful, dark-eyed Josefa.

He loved Josefa dearly and wanted to be with her. But there was no work for him in Taos. Within three months, Kit was hunting buffalo again for Bent's Fort. Then he heard that John Charles Frémont was setting out on another expedition. Mounting his horse, he rode off to join him.

This time he led Frémont's party far beyond South Pass. There was already a rough road through the pass. It had been made by the wagons of settlers who were bound for the Oregon country, and for the Sacramento Valley in California.

Frémont hoped to find other easy passes through the mountains which other settlers might use. He also wanted to explore parts of California which belonged to Mexico. So they started south over the Sierra Mountains.

It was winter. The snow in the mountains was deep. Food became scarce. Horses died of starvation. Before long, many of the men wanted to turn back. But not Frémont. And not Kit Carson. He had already been to California, trapping beaver with Ewing Young.

"It's the prettiest country you've ever laid your eyes on," he told the men. "All we got to do is get over these mountains. Put on your snowshoes now, and let's keep going."

They kept going. And one day Kit led Frémont's band of ragged, hungry men out of the mountains and into the beautiful Sacramento Valley. Soon they reached a big fort which had been built by a man named Sutter. There they rested and bought supplies. Then they rode farther south, past Indian villages, and ranches owned by wealthy Mexicans, and farms where Americans had settled. At last they turned east and headed home, through wild, unsettled country.

One April day they reached the Spanish Trail which led to Santa Fe. Late that afternoon they stopped as usual to make camp under some cottonwood trees. The horses and mules were hobbled. Fires were built, and the men cooked supper.

When Kit finished his meal, he wiped his mouth on the back of his hand. Then he sprawled on the ground, puffing on his pipe and thinking about Josefa. Suddenly he heard a commotion behind him. He jumped to his feet just as two Mexicans, a man and a half-grown boy, burst into camp.

The boy's name was Pablo, the man's was Fuentes. They were worn out with running and almost too breathless to speak. But Fuentes gasped out their story. They had been traveling with four other Mexicans—Fuentes' wife, Pablo's mother and father, and another man. With them they had thirty horses.

During the night a hundred Indians had attacked their camp. Fuentes and Pablo had escaped with the horses, but the other Mexicans had all been captured.

"Where are the horses now?" Frémont asked.

"We left them at Tomasa Spring," Fuentes said. "They were too tired to go any farther."

Pablo choked back a sob. "My mother!" he wailed. "My father!"

"We'll help you if we can," said Frémont. And Kit cried promptly, "Let's get started."

Pablo and Fuentes were given horses. In no time, Frémont and his men were pounding after them toward Tomaso Spring. When they reached it they found that the Indians had been there before them. Not a horse was left.

"We can trail them," Kit told Frémont. "We'd better hustle, too, if we aim to save those Mexicans. We can't tell what the Indians will do with them."

"And I can't risk sending my men any farther," Frémont replied soberly.

"I can go on alone," Kit said. Then he smiled when a scout named Godey cried, "I'll go with you."

Together he and Godey started after the Indians. It was growing dark and the tracks of the horses led through a gloomy mountain pass. But Kit Carson was one of the best trailers in the West. When he could no longer see the tracks, he dismounted now and then, and felt the ground with his hand to make sure that they were there.

At last the night closed in, inky black. Then the two men stopped to rest. With the first

[*143*]

light of day they started off again. Just at sunup they saw the herd of stolen horses ahead of them. Beyond the horses were nearly forty Indians. They were gathered in front of four big skin tents, cooking horsemeat.

Kit slid quickly from his saddle and motioned to Godey to do the same. The two men hid their horses behind some rocks. Dropping to their knees, they crawled stealthily toward the herd. Suddenly one of the stolen horses whinnied. The Indians sprang up in alarm and ran for their bows and arrows. Kit tightened his grip on his rifle.

"It's time to charge them," he whispered.

Godey nodded. Whooping wildly, he and Kit raced toward the camp, shooting as they ran. Two Indians dropped to the ground. The others fled into the hills, thinking that they were being attacked by a large force of men.

"I reckon they never dreamed there was only two of us," Godey said, as he and Kit rounded up the horses some time later.

Kit grinned. "We made enough noise for twenty," he said. "All we got to do now is to rescue them Mexicans."

But it was too late for Kit and his com-

They raced toward the camp, shooting as they ran

panion to save the four Mexicans who had been captured. They found that the Indians had already killed them.

Kit Carson and Godey did not feel that they had done anything remarkable in attacking nearly forty Indians and saving the herd of horses. That was all in the day's work for them.

But Lieutenant Frémont thought differently. When he made out his next report he wrote the story of the two brave men who had risked their lives to help the unknown Mexicans.

Later this report, like the others, was printed in many Eastern newspapers. And Kit's fame as a brave leader and scout began to spread through the East as it had through the West.

Meanwhile Kit had gone home to Taos. He had promised Frémont he would return to California with him if the young lieutenant made another trip to that Mexican province. But he hoped he would never have to leave Josefa again.

CHAPTER FIFTEEN

Kit Is Disappointed

A LONG line of men rode slowly down the dusty California road which led to the town of Monterey. The hot July sun glinted on the knives they wore at their waists, on their heavy revolvers and polished rifles.

Kit shifted his reins from one hand to another and drew the sleeve of his blue flannel shirt across his face. The man riding beside him sighed.

"Kind of warm, ain't it?" he asked.

Kit nodded but did not reply. He glanced at Captain Frémont, riding at the head of the line, surrounded by a bodyguard of five Indians. Then he turned in his saddle and looked at the men behind him. They were coming right along, even though their ponies were drooping their heads in the heat.

[*147*]

"Yep, it's kind of warm," he thought as he faced front again, "and kind of funny, me being in an army. I got to remember how it all came about so's I can tell Josefa when I get home."

In his mind he began to go over all the things that had happened to him in the past ten months. He remembered the day in August when he'd got word that Frémont was starting off for California again. And the day they'd all set out together from Bent's Fort.

They were just going to explore some more in California, Frémont told him. But when they got there, they ran into trouble right away.

The Mexicans were getting tired of having Americans come to settle in California. And the American settlers were getting tired of being ruled by Mexicans. So fighting had started.

At last forty American settlers had captured a little Mexican fort called Sonoma. They ran up a flag with a picture of a grizzly bear on it and said, "California's a republic now."

"But saying it was a republic sure didn't make it one," Kit said to himself.

He thought of the day that he and Frémont and all Frémont's men had marched to Sonoma to help the Americans hold the fort. They'd had a fine fandango there to celebrate the Fourth of July and then Frémont had

formed an army of his own men and a lot of settlers. He'd hardly started to drill them, though, when he heard news. Big news. The United States had declared war on Mexico!

It was all because of land that Mexico owned and the United States wanted. Texas had broken away from Mexico and become part of the United States. And now thousands of Americans believed that New Mexico and California should belong to the United States too.

Frémont certainly believed it. As soon as he heard that war had been declared, he had started out to capture the Mexican town of Monterey.

"Seems like it's already been captured, though," Kit thought, as he spied an American flag flying over the town.

And it had been! There was an American warship in the harbor, with an American commodore named Stockton in command. He ordered Frémont and his men aboard a sloop and sent them sailing south to capture San Diego. That was easy, because, when they reached there, they found that the Mexicans had fled.

So they marched north to Los Angeles. Kit figured there was sure to be a good scrap before they could take that town. But they were able to march right in with a brass band playing and people watching along the streets.

Los Angeles was the capital of the country and it looked now as though California was really conquered. Stockton and Frémont decided that the time had come to send the good news to the President of the United States.

Because of his courage and honesty, Kit Carson was chosen to make the long, dangerous, important journey to Washington. He chose fifteen of his best men to go with him. Six of them were Indians.

When the time came for him to leave, Frémont had a surprise for Kit. He made a little ceremony of it. Kit was told to line up his men on their mules in the plaza of Los Angeles. There he found Colonel Frémont and his little army waiting for him.

Colonel Frémont, on his splendid warhorse, faced Kit, who sat quietly in his saddle. He handed a rolled paper to the little gray-eyed man.

"Kit," he said, "this is your commission as

[*151*]

Lieutenant in the Army of the United States.
You've more than earned it."

Kit Carson took the paper, too flabber-
gasted to speak. But everyone else began to
cheer and yell like wild men. When they had
quieted down a little, Frémont passed a water-
proofed envelope to Kit.

"Lieutenant Carson," he said. "You will
deliver these papers to President Polk in the
White House in Washington. They tell the
news that California is now part of the United
States. To carry these dispatches across the
country is a tough job. The news must reach
Washington as quickly as possible. If anyone
can get it there safely, you can."

Frémont stretched out his hand and Kit
grasped it. "Good-by, Lieutenant Carson,"
said the colonel, "and good luck!"

"Thank you, Colonel," said Kit.

He wheeled his horse and signaled to his
men. Amid another burst of cheers, they
trotted out of the plaza toward the dry, red
mountains.

Kit was pleased at the honor which had
come to him.

" 'Tain't every man who gets to talk to the

When the time came to leave, Frémont had a surprise for Kit

President," he thought, as he and his men were riding past a peaceful little village in New Mexico several weeks later. "On my way back, I'll stop in Taos and see Josefa, too."

Then he squinted his eyes and peered across the prairie. A strange caravan of soldiers was coming toward them.

"Must be a whole army," Kit remarked as the soldiers drew nearer. "That's a general up front. He's got stars on his collar. I wonder what place he's aiming for."

He watched the army approach. Half a dozen officers rode behind the general. Then came two cannon, each drawn by six mules. A column of foot soldiers marched behind the cannon. They were followed by a long train of wagons which were carrying supplies.

All at once a rider on a tall bay horse came galloping past the infantry. He touched his hat as he swept past the general.

Kit recognized his old friend Fitzpatrick almost as soon as he saw him. Fitz raised his hand, palm forward, which was the Indian sign of greeting. Kit did the same.

"Kit, you old wolf!" the rider shouted as he slowed to a stop.

"Haugh, Fitz," Kit said. "Where'd you get that fellow with the stars? Who is he?"

"General Stephen Watts Kearny," Fitz answered with a grin. "And those men tailing after him are the Army of the West."

"What are you doing with them?" Kit asked.

"I joined up with them at Bent's Fort, and we've just been capturing New Mexico," Fitz told his friend. "We took it all without a battle, too. Didn't even have to fire a shot to capture Santa Fe. Now we're off to conquer California."

"Why, me and Frémont done that already," Kit drawled with a twinkle in his eye. "California's conquered and I'm carrying the good news to Washington. And, Fitz," he added sternly, "call me Lieutenant."

Fitz laughed. But before he could say anything more, the general and his staff of officers rode up.

"General Kearny," Fitz said, "this is an old friend of mine, Lieutenant Kit Carson. He's carrying dispatches from California."

The general frowned. "Can't these wild mountain men ever learn to salute?" he thought. Then he asked Kit where he was going and why. As Kit told his story, General Kearny's face grew darker and darker. Finally he interrupted him angrily.

"Frémont had no right to do what he has done!" he said hotly. "He had no orders from Washington. *I've* been sent to conquer California. Carson, you're the best guide in the West. I want you to turn back and lead me to California by the shortest route you know."

Kit shook his head. "I reckon I can't do that," he said quietly. "I promised I'd give these here papers to President Polk and—"

"You're a lieutenant in the Army, aren't you?" barked Kearny. "Then you'll obey the orders of your superior officers! Fitzpatrick will take your dispatches to Washington, and you'll return to California with me."

For a moment Kit said nothing. Now he would have no chance to see the East. No chance to talk to the President. No chance to visit with Josefa. At last, trying to hide his anger and disappointment, he handed his dispatches to Fitzpatrick. The next morning he watched his old friend ride off with them toward the rising sun.

CHAPTER SIXTEEN

The Battle of San Pasqual

KIT looked over General Kearny's army.

"General," he said, "you've got about eight hundred miles of hard, hot sandy trail ahead of you. With those wagons it'll take you four months."

"What do you advise, Carson?" the general asked.

"Take your mules out of harness. Pack your supplies on some of them. Mount your men on others. Then you'll get there in six weeks."

Kearny was silent for a few moments.

"I'll take a hundred men," he said at last, "and leave the rest here."

Kit thought this was a poor idea, but he couldn't make Kearny see why. So they went on with only a hundred men, plus Kit's fifteen. Luckily they took along the two cannon.

They were heading for the village of San Diego, close to the Pacific Ocean. With Kit guiding them, the little army rode steadily along, day after day. Early in December they reached California. A young American captain and some soldiers came riding down the trail to meet them.

Captain Gillespie brought news to General Kearny. At last the Mexicans had really begun to fight!

"Commodore Stockton's in San Diego," the captain told the general. "He'll be glad when you and your men get there, sir. He's almost surrounded by Mexicans and he's expecting real trouble."

Kearny nodded stiffly and ordered his men to ride on more quickly. Late in the afternoon they saw in the distance a village called San Pasqual. Kit and the advance guard of sixteen men galloped ahead. Before long they spotted several mounted Mexican soldiers stationed near the village. The Mexicans carried long, sharply pointed lances.

"I'll bet a buffalo hide they've been put there to watch for us," Kit thought. "They'll

[158]

try to trick us into chasing them, and then half the Mexican army will pounce out from somewhere and rub us out."

He turned to go back and warn Kearny. But at that moment the general came galloping toward him, far ahead of his army. He, too, had seen the Mexicans.

"Charge!" he shouted to the advance guard.

"Wait!" Kit yelled. "It's a trap! It's—"

"Charge!" the general shouted again.

There was nothing to do but obey. The Americans galloped toward the enemy, shooting as they rode. Wheeling their horses, the Mexicans sped toward the village. The Americans clattered after them with Kit in the lead.

Suddenly Kit's horse stumbled, throwing Kit to the road in the path of the oncoming mules. Kit rolled quickly out of the way, bruised and choking with dust. Stumbling to his feet, he looked for his rifle, which had flown from his hand. He found it under a prickly manzanita bush—broken.

He ran on toward the village, snatching up the rifle of a man who had been killed. The rattle of gunfire sounded ahead. He could see the Americans in the advance guard still rid-

ing after the Mexicans. Then suddenly the
Mexicans turned. And now there were nearly
two hundred of them.

With lances lowered, they came tearing
back. The Americans stood their ground. Just

then the rest of Kearny's little army galloped up and passed Kit. The mules drawing the cannon went rattling by. They wheeled into position. The mules were unhooked in a flash. The cannon were loaded.

"F-I-R-E!" shouted the officer in charge.

The guns roared. But the Mexicans were already retreating. The cannon balls rolled at the hoofs of their horses.

Then, before the gunners knew what was happening, two Mexicans came charging out of the brush, twirling ropes. As they swept past the cannon, they lassoed one of them. Whooping and laughing, they rode off, dragging it away.

By this time the other Mexicans had disappeared into the hills. And along the dusty road, thirty-six Americans lay dead or badly wounded. Kit and the other men who had not been hurt went to work to bury the dead. They carried the wounded into the shelter of some rocks on a hillside. There they spent a dreadful night.

At daybreak General Kearny ordered his army to march. They would soon be in need of water and Kit hoped that they could reach a little river he knew of, before dark. But the Mexican cavalry attacked them again and forced them to take cover on another rocky hill. There they spent another dreadful night, with little water and only mule meat for food. Again, in the morning, General Kearny wanted to push on.

"We can't do it, General," Kit said. "As

sure as the sun rises, those Mexicans are lying in wait for us up ahead."

"They'll wipe us *all* out if we march now!" exclaimed one of the officers.

"Well, we can't stay here," Kearny said impatiently.

A young officer named Beale spoke up.

"General," he said, "if you'll wait till dark, I'll try to get through to San Diego to get help from Commodore Stockton. Maybe Carson will let me take one of his Indians."

"I'll do more than that," Kit said. "I'll go with you. With three of us, there's a chance that one might get through."

Kearny grunted. "How far is San Diego?"

"Thirty miles," Kit replied.

"And you think you can get past those sentries?"

Kit looked down at the mounted sentries which the Mexicans had stationed around the hill. There were three lines of them, all armed with sharp, shining lances.

"I reckon we can make it if we're careful," Kit said.

"All right," agreed the general gruffly. "But if it doesn't work—" He left the rest of his thought unspoken.

The day dragged by slowly. At dusk, Kit, Lieutenant Beale, and the Indian filled their canteens with water. When the sun had set and its light gone out, they left their shelter. From rock to rock and from bush to bush they crept down the hill.

They were nearing the first line of sentries, when Beale's canteen scraped against a stone. Kit took off his own canteen and left it on the ground. He whispered to the others to do the same. It was better to risk dying of thirst than to be killed on this dismal hillside. Better to go barefoot, too. Beale and Kit took off their shoes and stuck them in their belts.

A Mexican officer rode past with a relief detail of guards. The three flattened to the ground and lay as still as the rocks. Kit heard the officer speak.

"They're bound to send out Carson," he said. "He's tricky. If anything moves, stick it. You might only get a horny toad. But take no chances."

"Running one of those long lances through a man on the ground would be easier than spearing fish," Kit thought, holding his breath. He felt Beale, beside him, shudder.

The three men wormed forward on their stomachs. At the second line of sentries a horseman almost stepped on them. He dismounted and pulled a metal-covered wick from his pocket. Then he struck flint and steel.

Kit blinked as the wick flared in the dark. If the sentry had looked around in the light of that flare, he couldn't have failed to see them. But he lit a cigarette, blew out the light, and moved on.

Kit dragged himself like a snake over the stony ground. His hands and feet were full of cactus spines. His knees and elbows were bruised and sore. Each minute seemed like an hour. But he knew that Beale must be suffering more. The lieutenant hadn't been hardened as Kit had.

Again and again Kit and his companions had to stop. But at last they passed the third line of sentries and reached the river. They drank thirstily, rested, and went on.

By this time both Beale and Kit had lost their shoes. Thirty hot, waterless miles of walking lay ahead of them. For men who lived in the saddle, this was tough. They weren't used to walking.

Night passed and the sun rose. All day long it beat down on them. Their feet were scratched, bruised, and swollen. Each step forward was harder than the last. But hour after hour through the hot day, the three men plodded on. Their tongues swelled. Their sore bodies throbbed with pain.

The cool of evening brought a little relief. At last, far ahead, they saw the lights of the little village of San Diego. They stood on a hill and felt a touch of dampness in the breeze that came in from the sea.

"We've got to separate," Kit said thickly.

"That'll give us three chances to get in. The Mexicans probably have guards all around the town."

Kit knew the lay of the land. The Indian, who had worn moccasins, was in the best shape and had the best chance to reach Commodore Stockton. So Kit gave him the easiest trail to travel. Kit showed Beale the next easiest. He himself took the hardest.

Kit's trail led through thick brush, uphill and downhill over rough ground. It was almost midnight when he reached San Diego and was stopped by an American sentry.

"Who's there?" rang out in the still night.

"Kit Carson," the tired scout answered hoarsely.

A few moments later Kit was entering the cool, thick-walled adobe hut which Commodore Stockton used as his headquarters.

Commodore Stockton was sitting at a table, reading by the dim light of an oil lamp. He got up as Kit limped toward the table.

"Sit down, man," he said, with sympathy in his voice.

Kit eased himself into a chair and reached for a bottle of water on the table.

[*168*]

As he drank, Commodore Stockton told him, "The Indian got in at seven-thirty. We sent help out to Kearny right away. Beale didn't get here till after ten."

"Lucky he made it at all, the shape he was in," Kit croaked. "He was out of his head for a while."

Stockton nodded. "He told me you almost carried him part of the way. He said he wouldn't have made it without your help. We put him right to bed. He'll be there a long time."

"Beale's got a lot of courage," Kit remarked.

"He's not the only one," Stockton added. "The people of the United States owe you a debt, Kit. If it weren't for men like you, this country might have stopped growing just west of the Mississippi River. Now, I think you'd better get some rest."

Kit smiled wearily. "I reckon I could use some," he agreed.

CHAPTER SEVENTEEN

The Biggest Fight of All

O N A warm spring afternoon Kit Carson
sat on the long low porch of his house at Taos,
quietly smoking his pipe. Many years had
passed since the battle at San Pasqual, and
many things had happened.

There had been more fighting with the
Mexicans and then California had really become a part of the United States. Again Kit
Carson had been sent to carry dispatches to the
President. And this time he'd made it, too,
clear to Washington. What a time he'd had
there!

He smiled wryly as he remembered the stiff
store clothes he had worn. And the tight store
shoes that had pinched his feet all during his
visit at the White House. He hadn't liked

[*170*]

Washington much. There'd been too many houses too close together. And too many people surrounding him, all talking about the brave things he'd done in the West.

"There've been hundreds of men who've done things braver than this old hoss," Kit had told them.

But they hadn't believed him, and he'd been glad to get away. When he reached home, he had told Josefa he hoped he'd never have to leave her again.

It seemed to him he'd hardly settled down, though, when the Government had another job for him to do.

Thousands of people were moving into California. Long wagon trains creaked over the plains toward the West, day after day. Buffalo were leaving the country, and the Indians were restless.

Angrily they attacked the wagon trains again and again, killing hundreds of settlers. The Army couldn't handle them all. So the Government had appointed Indian agents to help, and to try to make peace between the Indians and the white men.

Kit Carson had been one of the first men

chosen for this job. He was also one of the best, for the Indians trusted him. They could talk to him easily, because he had learned the languages of several tribes. And they knew he would not fight them unless he had to.

Since he had become an agent, Kit had led army men in several successful battles against the Indians. Between fights he had always hurried home to Josefa and his four children.

Now, as the sun began to sink in flames behind the high blue peaks near Taos, Josefa came to stand in the doorway behind him. And the children appeared around the corner of the house.

Bill, the oldest, was carrying his father's old rifle. Kit Junior was twirling a lariat. And Teresina was leading little Charles, who was just old enough to toddle.

The children were tired of play. Bill and Teresina sank down on the low porch steps. Charles climbed up on his father's knee. And young Kit leaned against his father's shoulder.

"Tell us a story, Pop," he said. "The one about the fight at 'Dobe Walls."

"Why, I've told you that a dozen times," replied his father.

"We still like it. Tell it again," Teresina demanded.

"But I'm sick of war," Kit declared. "Why, I never, but once, was in a fight I wasn't forced into. Now, the best days I ever spent were trapping. I could tell you—"

"It's not so exciting," Bill interrupted. "We want the story about Adobe Walls."

Kit sighed. "All right," he said. "You've got me outnumbered and a wise Injun never fights when he sees he's licked."

With one arm around Charles, he stoked his pipe and began.

"It was last summer and the Injuns were on the warpath again. They'd been raiding, burning ranches, running off stock, and attacking wagon trains. It was so bad no one could move on the plains without a big escort of cavalry. So General Carleton told me to put a stop to it.

"We figured a lot of Injuns would be going into winter camp down in Texas. There'd be Comanches, Kiowas, Arapahoes, and Plains Apaches all together and they'd camp along the Canadian River. So we aimed to make our headquarters at Adobe Walls. That was an old fort on the river that the Bents had quit using.

[*173*]

"I had fourteen officers and three hundred men. Besides that I took along seventy-two of my Injun friends as scouts, and twenty-seven supply wagons, and—"

"Pop," young Kit broke in, "why did General Carleton pick you over all those regular officers?"

"Don't interrupt," Bill told his brother. "You know Pop's the best Indian fighter in the West."

"You're exaggerating, son," Kit drawled. Then he went on with his story.

"Well," he said, "we left for Texas early in November. When we reached the Canadian River we headed east. Pretty soon we sighted the tops of Indian lodges over a ridge. It was a Kiowa village and my scouts reported that no one was there. But they said there was a big band of Injuns camping near Adobe Walls, 'way ahead.

"I sent the cavalry up to attend to them. But I stayed back with the howitzers. We only had two of them and I figured they'd come in right handy in a big battle."

"What's howitzers?" Teresina piped up.

"Howitzers," Kit replied, "are short cannon

[174]

that can be pointed up to fire over hills. They were pulled by mules and had to go pretty slow. A lieutenant named George Pettis was in charge of them.

"So I came along with Pettis. It wasn't long before we heard firing up ahead. It sounded like the Injuns were putting up a good fight. The howitzers kept tipping over. And after a while I had to leave Pettis to manage them, and ride up ahead to the fort.

"It was kind of tumbling down, but still good enough to give us some protection. The cavalry soldiers had put their horses inside. And the soldiers were all strung out in a long line outside the fort, lying in the tall grass and trying to shoot about two hundred Indians out of their saddles.

"Not far off other Injun villages were spread out over the river bottom. And between me and the nearest village, a big crowd of about thirteen hundred warriors were sit-

ting on their horses. A dozen chiefs, all foofa-
raw and feathers, were riding up and down,
making speeches to them.

"The Injuns who were fighting were yelling like mad. But not so loud that I couldn't
hear Pettis come galloping up with his mules
and cannon. He stopped and saluted me.

" 'Pettis,' I said, 'throw a few shells into that
crowd over there.'

" 'Battery halt!' Pettis ordered.

" 'Action right! Load with shell!

" 'Number one, *FIRE!*

" 'Number two, *FIRE!*" '

[*177*]

The children were holding their breaths. Their shining eyes never left the mild-looking man in the hide-bottomed rocking chair.

Kit reached into his pocket for his doeskin pouch.

"Go on, Pop," young Kit said tensely.

"Well, you should have seen those Injuns scatter!" Kit exclaimed. "They made for their villages like they'd seen a ghost. If it hadn't been for those howitzers, your old Pop might not be sitting here now. Any time those redskins made up their minds they wanted to pay the price, they could have wiped us right off the prairie.

"They didn't stay away long either. All afternoon they kept charging in, trying to pick us off without getting killed themselves. Believe it or not, they almost got so they could dodge those howitzer shells.

"And more Injuns kept coming in. Before dark there were three thousand of them, all with plenty of guns and ammunition. That was the most Injuns that ever got together for a fight—or ever will."

"But you held them off, didn't you, Pop?" asked Bill.

"Yep, we held 'em off. And finally we drove 'em back. All night we were afraid they'd come on us in the dark. But they didn't, and next morning they seemed to be gone. The army men wanted to chase them and attack 'em again.

"But I said, 'Not on your life. We're going home. This hoss has kept his hair a long time. And not by charging three thousand Injuns with three hundred soldiers.'

"Maybe they thought I was scared. Well, I was. And if they'd known Injuns like I do, they'd have been scared, too."

"Did General Carleton think you did right?" asked Teresina.

"Yes, he did," her father replied. "We'd killed a hundred Injuns and all we'd lost was two men. And the fact is, that fight stopped the raiding. There's been no wars with the Injuns since."

Bill said, "So you put a stop to the Indian wars, Pop."

"Well, I helped some, boy," Kit drawled.

He was silent for a moment, puffing on his pipe, and looking out at the full moon which was rising over the beautiful shining moun-

[*179*]

tains. Josefa came out and put her hand on his shoulder.

"Beautiful, isn't it, Kit?" she said.

"Yes," Kit said slowly. "Seems funny how folks could live in such a country and go on fighting and killing. I reckon there never would have been such trouble if all the white men and the Injuns had treated each other decent. But we drove off the Injuns' buffalo and we took their land. Maybe what we got from them served us right. I don't know."

He stood up and set little Charles on his feet. Then he reached for his old rifle, which Bill still held across his knees.

"I hope you'll never have to use a gun like I have, son," he said, running his hand over the brass tacks in the stock. "Fight if you must, like I did. But never forget that the biggest fight of all is for peace."

About the Author

EDMUND COLLIER was born into a very strict, respectable New England family. But from his seafaring ancestors he had inherited the wanderlust and so, at an early age, he left home. He headed west seeking adventure, and became a cowboy for a while. Then he served in the regular army and later joined the Forestry Service. All this time, his talent for writing was developing, and it was not long before he began to have his stories accepted by magazines dealing with cowboys and western life. Later he became the publisher and editor of WEST MAGAZINE. He is married, has three children, and at present lives in New York City.

About the Artist

FROM THE TIME Nick Eggenhofer started to read, as a youngster in Bavaria, Germany, tales of the Western range fascinated him. On arriving in the United States, he worked in New York as a laborer, shoe clerk, machinist, and lithographer. Evenings, he studied at Cooper Union. But when his day's work was done, he painted watercolors of cowboys—for fun. A publisher bought them all, and asked him to illustrate magazine stories of the West. To gather cowboy lore, he made many trips to the far West, and brought back a treasure trove of saddles, bridles, ten-gallon hats, and rifles. He and his wife and daughter now live in New Jersey.

"Names That Made History"

ENID LAMONTE MEADOWCROFT, *Supervising Editor*

THE STORY OF LAFAYETTE
By Hazel Wilson.   *Illustrated by Edy Legrand*

THE STORY OF ROBERT E. LEE
By Iris Vinton.   *Illustrated by John Alan Maxwell*

THE STORY OF ABRAHAM LINCOLN
By Nina Brown Baker.   *Illustrated by Warren Baumgartner*

THE STORY OF FLORENCE NIGHTINGALE
By Margaret Leighton.   *Illustrated by Corinne B. Dillon*

THE STORY OF LOUIS PASTEUR
By Alida Sims Malkus.   *Illustrated by Jo Spier*

THE STORY OF POCAHONTAS
By Shirley Graham.   *Illustrated by Mario Cooper*

THE STORY OF MARCO POLO
By Olive Price.   *Illustrated by Federico Castellon*

THE STORY OF THEODORE ROOSEVELT
By Winthrop Neilson.   *Illustrated by Edward A. Wilson*

THE STORY OF MARK TWAIN
By Joan Howard.   *Illustrated by Donald McKay*

THE STORY OF GEORGE WASHINGTON
By Enid LaMonte Meadowcroft.   *Illustrated by Edward A. Wilson*

THE STORY OF MAD ANTHONY WAYNE
By Hazel Wilson.   *Illustrated by Lawrence Beall Smith*

HANDSOME BOOKPLATES

If you would like a set of bookplates, so that you can write your own name in these books just the way the great signatures are shown, send your name and address to SIGNATURE BOOKS, GROSSET & DUNLAP, INC., 1107 Broadway, New York 10, N. Y. *We will mail you, upon receipt of ten cents to pay the cost of postage and handling, a set of handsomely designed bookplates, each one different.*